DEATH
ON DARK
WINGS

DEATH ON DARK WINGS

THOMAS A. DAVIS

Review and Herald Publishing Association Washington, D.C. 20012

Editor: Kit Watts
Layout: Floyd Tucker
Cover: Hélcio Deslandes

Photo credits:
British Ministry of Defense, p. 12
British Combine Photos, Ltd., p. 14
Imperial War Museum, pp. 27, 42, 46, 52,
59, 84, 104, 109, 123, 135
Duane S. Johnson, p. 142
Other photos supplied by the author.
War photos of planes, POW camps, etc.,
chosen for similarity to those described in this book.

CONTENTS

Is This What Death Is Like?

SERGEANT JOHN CURNOW sat up
with a start from the map table over which
he had been sagging asleep. A loud ripping
explosion echoed in his brain. His mind,
previously tired and blurred from several
nights' loss of sleep, was crystal clear.

Moving rapidly by the light of the
small lamp above his navigator's table
he reached down, picked up his parachute
from the floor, and buckled it on. He knew
instinctively what had happened. The
Lancaster bomber had been hit by an
antiaircraft shell.

Then swiftly he rose from his seat,
at the same time unclipping the oxygen
line from his oxygen mask, and disconnect-
ing the intercom from his flying helmet.
Pulling aside the curtain to his compartment
he stepped into the pilot's cabin.

A pale quarter moon off to port in the
almost cloudless sky and the subdued
green light from the pilot's instrument
panel illuminated the cabin dimly.
Roper, the pilot, was in his seat looking
ahead steadily, his hands holding the
controls. His flying helmet gleamed
above the upturned collar of his Irvin

coat. His eyes were narrowed above his oxygen mask. He glanced at John, then faced forward once more. Rose, the engineer, was not at his station beside him.

The plane was flying on a level course, and the four deep-pulsing engines were running smoothly.

Quickly John clipped into an oxygen outlet and connected with intercom.

"Where's Rosie?" he asked.

"Gone below." Roper's voice coming through the earphones in John's helmet above the roar of the engines had a metallic, unreal sound, as if a vast and lonely emptiness separated them.

John looked down beyond the few narrow steps at his feet leading to the dark opening of the bomb-aimer's cubicle at the nose of the plane, where Rose had disappeared. He could see nothing.

Roper was speaking again. "Can you see what the damage is?" He nodded toward the starboard side of the plane.

Leaning against the cold bare metal framework, John peered through the plexiglass of the canopy. By the pale light of the moon he could see the dark wing a few feet behind and below him, stretching away into the night. Almost directly in line with him the propellers of the two starboard engines whirred reassuringly.

Then he saw something that caused his heart to miss a beat.

Behind the inner engine about one third of the way from the trailing edge of the wing, tiny wraiths of flame were leaping and dancing around a hole.

"We're on fire! There's a hole about a foot across toward the back of the wing."

"Near the engine?"

"Yes."

"Perhaps we can put the fire out with the extinguisher."

Roper throttled back on the inner engine and feathered its propeller so that it no longer bit into the air.

"Push the extinguisher button."

John reached over to the control panel and pushed the button that activated the extinguisher built into the engine. He watched the wing for a few moments.

"The fire isn't going out. It's getting worse!"

John snatched up Roper's parachute. Rapidly he began to unstrap him from his seat so that the parachute could be fastened on. He knew that if the fire did not go out, which now seemed likely, they were in deadly peril. Fanned by the slip stream, it could burn through the wing in minutes, causing it to break off; or there could be a fuel explosion.

As he worked feverishly with the buckles he wondered about the other five members of the crew—Waghorn, in his lonely rear-gunner's turret at the extreme of the plane; Smith, the mid-upper gunner; Dobie, the wireless operator, in the small compartment directly behind his own; Rose, the engineer, down below in the bomb-aimer's station; and Todd, the bombardier-front gunner in his turret a few feet in front of the cabin at the nose of the plane. Would Munich, the city they had just bombed, be their last target? he wondered.

A frighteningly loud metallic bang from the burning wing rang sharply through the wounded ship. With the sound the aileron controls jerked a notch anticlockwise in Roper's hands. There was another bang, and then another, and another. And with each bang the controls jerked farther to the left.

Horrified, John guessed what was happening. The fire had destroyed the aileron controls in the wing. And each bang meant that the starboard aileron was swinging downward while the port aileron was automatically turning up. With each bang the right wing rose higher and higher, while the plane went into a steeper and steeper banking dive to port.

Everything was moving with lightning speed now. As

in a dream that lasted only a few seconds John was aware that Roper was off his seat, crouching, straining, uselessly throwing every ounce of strength and weight in a frantic battle for his life and the life of his crew against the relentlessly jerking, twisting controls.

Striving to maintain an ever-shifting balance in a plane that was out of control, John groped desperately to fasten Roper's parachute.

One parachute hook snapped into Roper's harness. Then suddenly John was thrown to the floor as though a giant hand had abruptly thrust him down.

The bomber had flipped upside down and begun a deadly spinning toward earth, some twenty thousand feet below in the darkness.

And John Curnow was bound helplessly by the invisible chains of centrifugal force inside the stricken bomber spiraling to fiery death, taking him with it.

Desperately he tried to move, but using every ounce of strength he could not lift even a hand from the floor. His chin was being pressed down and down into his chest as though a monstrous vise was steadily tightening about him.

A dreadful coldness that was not physical but like the icy hand of death closed over him. Through a mist and a horror of unreality the thought came: We are going to die. What is beyond?

As in a dream he could feel the plane spinning. Time seemed to be obliterated. He was spiraling, endlessly spiraling, through eternity.

A rending, roaring crash penetrated the dimness of half-consciousness.

We have hit the ground, he thought vaguely.

A great burst of brilliant, cosmic light engulfed him.

Is this what death is like? he wondered in the split second before oblivion swallowed him.

Days of Preparation

SUMMER, 1940. The Battle of Britain. It began in August when the Heinkel and Dornier bombers, the Junkers dive bombers, and Messerschmitt 109 and 110 fighters of the German Luftwaffe began to sweep over southeastern England in an attempt to destroy the Royal Air Force in the air and on the ground and thus set the stage for the invasion of England.

No one who lived through those days can forget the epic struggle in which a relative handful of R.A.F. fighter pilots rose in their Hurricane and Spitfire fighters to meet the invaders and fight them to a standstill. Nor can he forget the immortal tribute paid them by Winston Churchill: "Never in the field of human conflict was so much owed by so many to so few."

In September the issue was decided. The battle reached its peak and began to subside. And gradually over the following weeks the Luftwaffe was driven from England's daytime skies.

In the meantime the Germans had begun night as well as day bombing, and

11

No one who lived through those days can forget that epic struggle.

soon London became the center of attack.

The invasion of England was expected not merely by ships and barges from across the English Channel but also from the air. One of the most effective methods the Germans had used to defeat Belgium and Holland had been to drop parachute troops behind the lines. The British were determined not to be caught in this way.

The Home Guard was one answer to this threat. This volunteer force was composed of men young and old who by reason of health or age could not qualify for regular military service. There were some one million such volunteers scattered over the length and breadth of Great Britain. John Curnow was one.

John's home was in Ickenham, a picturesque village sixteen miles west of the center of London. There three nights a week he stood guard in the center of the village with an older companion and watched and listened to the awesome drama of a great city fighting for its life.

Across the miles the rising and falling wail of the air-raid sirens echoed. He heard the distant dry rattle of ack-ack guns and the ominous death rumble of exploding bombs. He watched the weaving searchlights like glowing tentacles groping to enfold a winged enemy, and gazed at the sullen red flames that welled like blood from the gaping wounds of night.

Occasionally an enemy bomber would be caught in a searchlight. Perhaps another light would succeed in joining the first before the plane could escape. Sometimes several searchlights would cone the high-flying bomber.

Fascinated, John watched the gray-black puffs of smoke from exploding shells as the gunners on the ground tried to bring the plane down. Sometimes a streamer of flame would suddenly appear, and the throbbing drone of the plane's engines would become a scream as it plunged toward earth marking a fiery path to death.

John witnessed all this with excitement mingled

With London burning John couldn't bear standing on the sidelines.

with deep frustration. He was not satisfied to be standing
on the perimeter, a mere spectator, even though he was
in the Home Guard. That was all very well for older
men, many of whom were veterans of World War I and
could no longer fight. He wanted to do more than be
ready for an invasion that might never come, or simply
wait for an enemy airman to fall out of the sky on a parachute. Small chance for that to happen in his vicinity!

He wanted to be in on the fight himself. He wanted
to get in his own blows.

But one seemingly insurmountable obstacle barred

his way for months to come. He was not quite seventeen. To be accepted for service a man had to be eighteen.

Then one day John met his friend Norman Howard on the street. Norman was about his own age.

"Guess what, John," Norman greeted him.

"What?"

"I've joined the R.A.F."

"How come? You're too young."

Norman grinned. "I told 'em I was eighteen."

A few weeks later John turned seventeen.

One day as he was on his way to school he glanced at a wall. Confronting him was a picture of a young airman pointing sternly at him from a poster. "Your country needs you now! Join the R.A.F.," the legend said.

John looked the young man in the eye for a moment. He made up his mind.

Finding the nearest recruiting office he made himself as tall as his seventeen years allowed, assumed the fiercest expression his boyish face permitted, and strode through the door.

"I want to join the R.A.F.," he announced in his deepest voice to the recruiting sergeant sitting behind the desk in the little room.

The man looked him over appraisingly.

"What's your age?"

"Eighteen," John stated defiantly.

The next six months were a mixture of activity and inactivity, excitement and boredom. After being signed up by the recruiting officer, who obviously overlooked his youthfulness, John asked to be trained as a fighter pilot. He was told that there was no pilot's course beginning at the moment. However, they needed navigators for bombers. He could join a navigator's course that was starting "immediately."

Immediately proved to be more than six months later, after he had finished basic training, spent three months of a harsh winter doing guard duty at a small R.A.F. sta-

The recruiting officer asked his age. "Eighteen," John said defiantly.

tion in Scotland, and several more weeks doing the same at Newcastle-on-Tyne.

During his basic training, which he took at Winslow, an Air Force training station a few miles from Manchester, he was billeted in one of the station's gray wooden barracks, each of which had twenty-four occupants.

John soon discovered that there was keen competition among the occupants of the many huts to see which would win the commanding officer's commendation for neatness at the end of the six-week course.

John found himself with a group that was determined to be the ultimate in spit and polish. Not only were the beds lined up with almost calibrated precision, not only were the contents of each locker faultlessly arranged, not only were the windows and floors kept spotless, but the handles of the brooms were scraped regularly with a razor blade to make them look like new. The big galvanized-iron coalbox near the stove was kept shining with Brasso. And uniform-sized pieces of coal were chosen, shined with shoe polish, and arranged neatly on top of the other coal in the box. Whenever coal needed to be added to the fire the polished pieces were carefully laid aside, then replaced.

John's room won.

Eventually, in the spring of 1941, John found himself in Initial Training School at Torquay. There he learned the basics required of a bomber navigator, one of which was getting well in mind the silhouettes of enemy and allied aircraft so that one might recognize them immediately.

When John had finished he was ready for practical navigation training under actual flying conditions. This training, given under the Commonwealth Plan, was to be in either Canada or South Africa. John learned that he was to be sent to South Africa.

After a ten-day leave he said good-by to a serious-faced father and moist-eyed mother and traveled by train to West Kirby, in Cheshire. From there he was sent with a draft of about one hundred other airmen to Liverpool to join a ship scheduled to sail for South Africa.

The *Reno del Pacifica* was a medium-sized ship built to carry 350 passengers in peacetime. Now three-tiered bunks were fitted into all available space below deck, so that she was capable of accommodating about 2,000 men.

The ship slipped out of Liverpool harbor one gray morning and made her way up the west coast of England to the shelter of the broad estuary of the Clyde, in Scotland, where other ships, part of a large convoy, were waiting to sail.

The trip to Cape Town took seven weeks. The large convoy sailed across the Atlantic almost to Newfoundland, then slipped down the coast of North America, during which time some of the ships left the convoy. Most of the ships, including the *Reno del Pacifica,* continued across the South Atlantic to Africa, stopping briefly at Freetown, in Sierra Leone, for refueling. But instead of sailing south along the African coast, the convoy steered southwest for South America. Nearing the coast of that continent, it turned south, and did not sail toward Cape Town until almost at the latitude of that city.

John, with the other men on board, hoped that after their long weeks of confinement on ship they would be given a day or two of freedom in Cape Town. Most of them anticipated seeing the town and climbing Table Mountain. But R.A.F. transportation had other ideas. They were immediately hustled aboard a waiting train, and in a short time were rolling northward across South Africa through the hills and across the veldt. Their destination was an R.A.F. staging camp near Pretoria. There at last they were given ten days' leave.

John and two or three friends decided to spend their leave in Durban, on the Indian Ocean. John found Durban a beautiful and interesting city. He was especially

In twenty weeks John received Navigator/Bomb-Aimer's wings.

fascinated by the tall, majestic Zulus pulling rickshas and wearing colorful feathered headdresses. And he ate bananas, dozens of them, and drank gallons of milkshakes. In wartime England such luxuries were unavailable.

At the end of the ten days John and twelve other men taking the navigator's course were posted to Port Elizabeth on the south coast. Then their practical training began in earnest.

In two weeks they were flying on bombing and gunnery practice. Fairy Battle planes built for a pilot and one trainee were used. They would fly along the coast to a group of small rocky islands marked off for bombing. The pilot would fly in at a few thousand feet, and the bomb aimer, lying on his stomach in the belly of the plane, would aim for the bombing point, showing white below. Elation came when gray billows from the smoke bombs rose from the target. Almost as often there were groans when the targets were missed.

Navigator's training was done in twin-engined Avro Anson planes. One thing about the Avro Ansons John disliked intensely. They did not have hydraulic undercarriages. This meant that after the plane was airborne the wheels had to be cranked up by hand. It was the trainee navigator's job to do the cranking. It needed about two hundred turns of the crank to get them up, and it took just about everything John had to make the last few turns. Getting them down was easy—gravity looked after that.

Graduation came at the end of twenty weeks, at which time John received the coveted Navigator/Bomb-Aimer's wings and was given the rank of sergeant.

He found himself once again at Cape Town, from which port he and his group were to sail for England. This time he was able to climb Table Mountain before embarking on the *Empress of Japan,* which was on her way to England from the Far East.

There were only forty-five airmen aboard the ship. Among the passengers already on the ship when she arrived from the East were 150 survivors from torpedoed ships and 450 women and children refugees from Singapore.

The *Empress of Japan* was a fast liner that sailed without convoy, depending on her speed to escape enemy ships and submarines. No sign of the enemy was seen during the trip. Nevertheless, there was a continuous feeling of suspense and tension, which was met by an attitude of lightheartedness or frivolity on the part of some.

After fifteen days the ship sailed up the Irish Sea into

Liverpool. The feeling of relief experienced by all aboard was profound. Some of the women refugees who had lost everything, including their husbands, when the Japanese captured Singapore, broke down and wept.

After a brief leave at home John was given a six-week course at an advanced navigation center at Millom, Cumberland. From Millom he was posted to an operational training unit at Litchfield, in Staffordshire, near Burton-on-Trent.

John began to experience a keyed-up feeling and to notice symptoms of it in the others of his group. Up to then the whole thing had seemed like a bit of a lark. But Litchfield meant operational training—and operational training meant that in a short time they would be in the deadly serious business of war. The lark was just about over.

It was during operational training that permanent flying crews were formed. These were not formed arbitrarily. Each man was permitted to join the crew he felt he could work best with.

At noon on the day John arrived at the station he was standing in the mess hall looking around for some place to sit when someone called out, "Hey, Curnow!"

Looking in the direction from which the voice came he saw John Todd, whom his friends called Toddy. He had been one of the thirteen in John's group who had trained in South Africa. As they talked John learned that since his return from South Africa, Toddy had specialized as a bomb aimer, while John had stayed with navigation.

After a while Todd said, "Have you got a crew yet?"

"Not yet."

"Nor do I. How about teaming up together?"

John agreed. Todd was a quiet, steady fellow in his early thirties. He would be a dependable man to fly with.

That evening at supper Todd found John. "Say, I've found three other chaps who have teamed up together.

(L-R) Ernest Waghorn, John Roper, John Todd. (Front) John Dobie.

They need a navigator and a bomb aimer. Come and meet them after we eat."

They found the three men sitting together in the sergeants' mess lounge.

Toddy introduced John to the three.

It turned out that two of them also were named John. John Roper, the pilot, was a handsome military-type chap of twenty-three who looked the part of a pilot. He sported a small mustache, which he frequently brushed with the back of his forefinger. Roper gave the impression of being somewhat tense but self-controlled. John learned later that he had trained originally as a fighter pilot but had converted to bombers.

The other John was John Dobie, a stocky five-foot-four Scot with humorous blue eyes and, as Curnow soon discovered, a sense of humor to go with them. Dobie, who was in his early twenties, was a wireless operator.

The third man was Ernest "Waggie" Waghorn, the rear gunner. Waggie, a rather quiet chap, was a regular, having joined the R.A.F. before the war.

After two weeks of rather boring ground training John and his crew were sent to a satellite airdrome * at Tatten Hill, about ten miles from Litchfield. An intensive eight-week flying course welded them together as a flying team. This course was taken in Wimpies, as the twin-engined Wellington medium bombers were affectionately called. During this time John had his nineteenth birthday.

After two weeks of day flying they were put on night flying. This was an essential part of their training, for most of the bombing missions of the Royal Air Force were carried out at night. Consequently, it was imperative that the crew become thoroughly acquainted with night flying requirements and conditions.

Night flying during the training period usually entailed flying over a planned course, generally a triangular one. John, being navigator, was responsible for getting them over the course.

Before each flight there was a briefing session. The pilots and navigators were briefed separately.

On the front wall of the big briefing room was a large map of the British Isles. The squadron navigational officer would stick colored pins into the map to show the route to be followed on that particular night. Then he would tell the men the altitude at which to fly, the time it should take to reach each designated point, and weather conditions prevailing.

Each navigator had his own map for each particular flight. These maps were drawn to Mercator's projection, with longitudinal and latitudinal lines forming blocks

---

° Airdrome. British term for *airfield*.

representing twenty-five square nautical miles. The maps showed no towns or cities. On his map each navigator marked each position designated by the officer in its proper square, and noted other information.

One route was to take the fliers east to a deep indentation of water called The Wash, then southwest to the vicinity of Oxford, and north back to their station.

As the navigation officer was giving the bearings, he remarked, "There's one thing you'll need to watch, fellows. We're taking you pretty close to Rugby on this one. Rugby has barrage balloons * up. You wouldn't want to get mixed up with them."

At ten o'clock that night the Wimpies began to roar down the runway and disappear toward the east. A full moon etched the unrolling countryside in soft contrasts of light and shadow.

After their plane had taken off John stood near Roper for a while admiring the scene below. Then he squeezed himself into his tiny compartment with its small map table, switched on the shaded light, and went to work. His duties included getting radio bearings to fix their position, calculating wind speed and direction so as to keep on course, and keeping the log, in which time, position, and other pertinent information were recorded. Every once in a while he would stand in the bubble-shaped astrodome a few feet to the rear of his cubbyhole and take a fix by the stars. This method was not ordinarily used for navigation, but it was necessary that the navigator keep in practice in case the radio should not work sometime and bearings not be available from that source.

The whole flight was scheduled to take about two hours.

The Wimpy droned on its way out to The Wash, southwest to Oxford, then north toward Tatten Hill.

---

* Barrage balloons. A curtain of captive balloons raised above a defense area to trap enemy aircraft and prevent penetration.

Finally there was only about half of the last lap to go. John had checked the wind, which had changed a little. He knew that he was about three miles east of the exact flight route but was not concerned. The correction could be made easily. And according to his chart he was still four and one-half miles west of Rugby with its barrage balloons. There was nothing to be concerned about.

He was making a notation in the logbook when the voice of Waghorn, the rear gunner, came over the intercom. "I see a sausage-shaped lake below. Is there one on our route?"

Quickly John consulted his topographical map. No lake was indicated.

Then Todd, the bomb aimer, spoke. "I see one ahead! No! *It's a balloon!*"

Abruptly John was thrown back and sideways against his seat. The plane banked sharply until it was flying on its wingtip. In the moonlight Roper had suddenly seen a huge dark shape looming in front of him. Only this violent maneuver saved them from crashing into a balloon. He had to bank sharply three more times before they finally got out of the barrage.

When they were safely away from the balloons Roper's voice came grimly over the intercom, "What type of navigator have I got? If we ever get back alive I'm going to get myself a new one."

John, shaken and puzzled, couldn't figure out where he had gone wrong. After they landed, he checked the navigation officer's directions and discovered that he had indicated Rugby with its barrage balloons in the square to the right of the one he should have marked. John never made that kind of mistake again!

Right up to the time for the next day's training flight John didn't know whether he had a crew or not. But no more was said about the incident. At the end of the course both he and Roper were given a vote of confidence by the other three men in the crew.

Circle of Fire

"ALL RIGHT, MEN, this is your
lorry!" *

John climbed into the darkness of
the big covered lorry and found a place
between two other airmen on the wooden
seat. His parachute webbing was strapped
over his uniform. He carried his parachute,
his automatic sextant, and his bulging
navigator's bag containing maps, charts,
and other navigational equipment. In one
of his pockets was a package of German
and French currency, food tablets,
a small compass, and maps printed on silk,
in case he was shot down and survived.

Other men clambered aboard until
there were fourteen, making up two
crews. The lorry's motor roared, and with
a jerk they were rolling toward planes
waiting silently at their dispersal
points at the far side of the airdrome.

This is it, John thought to himself.
Only three weeks before, he and the
other four men had arrived at the station
at Elsham Wolds, Lincolnshire, to become
one of the crews of Royal Air Force 103
Squadron, Bomber Command.

At their station they had been converted

In the night a large shadow thundered past, lifting into the darkness.

to four-engine Halifax heavy bombers. Their new plane required that two more men be added to the crew—a gunner for the gun turret amidships and a flight engineer. The two new men were both named John. The mid-upper gunner was John Smith; the engineer was John Rose. The crew was now made up of six Johns and the lone Waggie Waghorn.

John thought of their mission for that night. He knew, and yet somehow he couldn't really grasp the fact, he couldn't believe, that in a few short hours their plane would be over a German city on their first mission of death. And as a result of them perhaps scores, perhaps hundreds, of people would die. They themselves might not return.

He shook off the thought.

Above the lorry's engine he heard another deep, more powerful roar, which grew louder. Looking out the end of the lorry into the night, he saw a large shadow thunder past and lift into the darkness. Squadron 103 was taking

° Lorry. In this case, a covered truck used to transport personnel.

off. Already several of the planes were circling the airport, each climbing to a predetermined altitude before heading out over the North Sea.

Several squadrons would be taking part in the raid tonight, they had been told during the briefing. Altogether some 350 planes from squadrons stationed all over the Midlands would converge on the strategic port of Kiel, on the Baltic Sea. Their objective was to destroy the submarine base there.

John reviewed the recent events leading up to this moment. He had first learned that tonight was "the" night when a sergeant from squadron office entered the sergeants' mess at four-thirty that afternoon while he was relaxing with other members of the crew.

"Attention, all air crews. Ops [operations] will be on tonight," the sergeant announced. "Pilots and navigators report at the navigation room at seventeen hundred hours. The main briefing will be at nineteen hundred hours."

John had looked at some of the men around him to see what their reactions were. Some tried to be nonchalant. In some he thought he detected signs of the anxiety he himself felt. Knots tied and untied themselves in his stomach.

By 5:00 P.M. twenty-four pilots and navigators had seated themselves on long benches in front of long wooden tables in the navigation room. The rest of the crew would attend the main briefing later. The fewer knowing the actual target until necessary, the better.

The senior squadron navigation officer had stood by a large map of Europe on a wall and announced in businesslike tones, "Well, men, the target for tonight is Kiel."

He wound a strand of colored wool around pins in the map to show their flight route. The plan was for the raiders to converge over Skegness on the north shore of The Wash, fly over the North Sea toward Denmark, far enough away from the Dutch and German coasts to avoid antiaircraft fire; and then cut across the Danish peninsula between Kiel and Lübeck. After getting some miles past the target, they were to swing around and approach the target area from the southeast.

The navigation officer had given details of height, speed, time of departure, and estimated time of arrival at the target.

The pilots had then left to check on the readying of the aircraft, leaving the navigators to work out their flight plans.

By 7:00 P.M. the eighty-four men of the crews of twelve Halifax bombers had gathered at the squadron briefing room for the main briefing. On the wall facing them were a big blackboard, a large map of Northern Europe, a detailed map of Kiel, and a projection screen.

Wing Commander Carter, the squadron commander, had stood at the front of the room and announced in his crisp, almost curt manner, "Well, gentlemen, operations are definitely on tonight. Please give careful attention to Squadron Leader Shepherd."

The lights had gone out, and a large photograph was thrown on the screen. Near the center was a red spot.

Squadron Leader Shepherd, the senior intelligence officer, had addressed the expectant airmen. "This, gentlemen, is Kiel, your target for tonight." He had pointed to the red spot, which lay over the docks area. "This is your aiming point. These are the submarine pens that must be destroyed." Todd and the other bomb aimers had been given a detailed map of the actual target area. He would study and memorize the main features of the area so that he could direct the pilot on the final bombing run.

The intelligence officer had gone on to explain the strategic and political significance of the raid.

Then a weather chart had been flashed on the screen, and a meteorological officer was talking, giving the latest weather information. This was to be an ideal night for an operation—no moon and just enough cloud to offer protection.

The lights had come on. The squadron commander again addressed the airmen, stressing the need for accurate bombing. He had paused briefly. Then he said, "Good luck to you, gentlemen." The briefing was over.

John had looked around at the other men with a sense of unreality. Again he had wondered whether they felt as he did. Why was he there? Where were the glamour and heroic feeling he had dreamed of while doing Home Guard at Ickenham? At the briefing he had sensed only futility—tragic futility. War! Killing! Death!

John broke away from his thoughts; the lorry was grinding to a stop.

"Roper's crew off here."

John and the others climbed out.

Over them loomed the dark hulk of their Halifax. The four-engine plane looked gargantuan to John. Until they had joined 103 Squadron the largest plane they had flown had been the twin-engine Wellington. He hadn't yet gotten used to the bigger Halifax.

The ground maintenance crew were moving around shining their flashlights here and there, checking to be sure that everything was in good order.

As the rest of the crew climbed into the plane John paused a moment and looked up at the stars shining between the scattered clouds. What lay ahead of him?

He clambered up the ladder inside the plane dragging his equipment. Looking down the dim interior toward the front, he could see Roper ready to sit down at the controls. Toward the rear, in the empty ribbed belly of the plane, Smith's legs dangled from his gun turret.

The headman of the plane's maintenance crew appeared in the hatch. He thrust a file of grimy papers at John. They were the release papers to be signed by the pilot.

John made his way to the front and handed them to Roper, who glanced at them casually, then wrote "J. Roper" on the designated line. John took them back and passed them to the waiting mechanic, who dropped to the ground and waved O.K.

John pulled up the metal ladder and slammed the door, sealing himself and the crew inside the plane.

Roper started the engines. Their roar filled the narrow fuselage.

With a feeling of unreality still gripping him, John made his way to his tiny compartment directly behind the pilot. He set out the navigational chart and checked his equipment as the heavily loaded bomber lumbered to the runway. As the plane swung around into position for take-off John took a standing position behind Rose, who was at Roper's right.

There was a short pause as Roper tested the engines for the last time. Then they were moving. The lights of the runway flashed past faster and faster.

John braced himself against the craft. A feeling of apprehension mingled with exhilaration flooded over him. It was an emotion he was to experience each time they took off on an operation.

There was a sudden surge of power as Rose, cued by Roper, pushed the throttle full forward for that final take-off burst and they were in the air. Returning to his compartment, John seated himself at his navigator's table, plugged into intercom, and turned to his charts. In a moment he gave Roper the course for Skegness.

When they were over Skegness, he gave the new course. Then he made his way to the astrodome, a hemisphere of plexiglass just behind his compartment from which he made his fixes by the stars. By now they had climbed to more than 5,000 feet, and Roper had given instructions for the crew to connect to the oxygen.

Standing in the astrodome without the illusion of protection afforded by the fuselage John looked up at the stars—faroff, clear, and serene. They seemed to be imbued with a quality of endless peace, he thought. He wished he had some of that himself.

About fifty miles from the Danish coast they altered course for the run between Lübeck and Kiel.

Now they were approaching the coast of Germany north of the East Frisian Islands. Roper's tense voice came over the intercom. "Watch it, chappies! Keep your eyes skinned for Jerry * night fighters!"

Then the coast of Germany was beneath them; they were flying across the narrow peninsula between Kiel and Lübeck. Ahead and to port they could see the red glow of burning Kiel. Some of the bombers already had been at work. Weaving searchlights were moving restlessly across the sky, searching for the enemy. Soon they would be searching for them!

Roper had begun the weaving flying pattern that he would maintain—except for the deadly dangerous time when they were making their final bombing run—until they were well away from the German coast on their way back home.

They were now about fifteen miles southeast of Kiel. In a moment they would swing around for the approach. John gave Roper directions for the approach to the target area, then began to work out his course for home. The bombing run would be visual. It was up to Todd, the bomb aimer, to take them over the target. As Roper was making the approach he would ask John for the course to set for home, so that he could take it as soon as the bombs were away.

With the navigation of the plane out of his hands for the time being, John left his compartment and stood in the pilot's cabin behind Rose.

They seemed to be flying into an inferno. The antiaircraft display ripped the night apart. Light flak was rising as from the nozzles of hundreds of lethal hoses, filling the night with flashing capricious patterns of red, green, and yellow. Above it the heavy flak burst into red, leav-

---

* A nickname for the Germans.

ing gray patches of smoke drifting through the sky.

And all around were the searchlights. John felt as though they were flying into a midday sun with every gun and every searchlight focused on them as they moved ever so slowly across the sky.

Straight into the midst of that flaming hell they went. Then suddenly the plane was filled with a blue glare. A sweeping searchlight had found them.

Immediately Roper threw the plane into a violent dive out of the sweep of the searchlight. John braced himself and hung on. In fearful fascination he watched. Already other searchlights were sweeping in to join the first—to catch their plane in a deadly cone of light from which there would be no escape.

But they had been in the searchlight's beam for only a split second. The lights swept the sky but failed to locate them. For now they had escaped.

Directed by the bomb aimer Roper flew, still weaving, toward the center of the target area.

"Hold it, Skipper. Bomb doors open." The voice was Todd's.

"Doors open," Roper replied as he leveled off for the nerve-wracking bombing run.

"Bombs away."

The plane lurched upward as the more than three and one-half tons of bombs fell away. For a few seconds longer Roper held the plane on its straight course, until the required aerial photo had been taken, then he threw the plane into a strong evasive turn.

John found himself sweating, yet cold from the intense strain. The bombing run had taken two minutes. To him it had seemed like twenty years.

He noted in his log the time the bombs were released: "0032 bombs gone."

They had battled to get inside the circle of death. Now the battle was to escape from it. The bursting shells seemed to multiply, sounding like the barking of monstrous dogs all around and below the plane.

Then they were outside the ring of fire, winging into darkness. The stars, far away, were clear and serene. The monotonous roar of the motors comforted them.

They were away from the worst but not all of the danger. Other antiaircraft guns below still could hit them. Or they could be attacked by a German night fighter.

"Coastline coming up, Navigator." It was Todd's voice. He had gone back to his guns in the turret at the nose of the bomber after releasing the bombs.

"Any chance of pinpointing a landmark for me?" John asked.

"A bit too dark for that, I think."

"What about Helgoland?" Roper broke in. "It's somewhere out here, and we don't want to get caught in *their* flak. That place bristles with guns."

John checked his map. "We came off the target on course, so we should pass about ten miles north of Helgoland. It's about thirty-five miles off the coast we've just left. We'll pass it in seven or eight minutes."

In a few minutes Roper's voice came over the intercom. "What time will we get to base?"

"About three o'clock," John answered. "With the wind we've got it will take us two hours from now. We are past Helgoland."

As time passed, John checked their progress on his chart and made the necessary entries in the logbook.

At last they were approaching their base, and the time came to make radio contact.

"Hello, Toddy, navigator here," John said. "We should be approaching the coast near Grimsby in a few minutes. Let me know if you see it."

"Righto! There's not much cloud, so I should be able to pick it up all right."

A few minutes of silence followed, then, "Coastline coming up, Curnow." Todd's voice carried a note of restrained excitement.

A few more minutes, and John said, "We're almost at our airport, Skipper."

"Hello, B-Bottie,* hello, B-Bottie." Roper was calling the control tower.

"Hello, B-Bottie. This is D-Donald calling. D-Donald calling. Request permission to pancake. Over."

"Hello, D-Donald, this is B-Bottie. You may pancake. You may pancake."

"D-Donald calling. Pancaking. Pancaking. Over."

Roper circled into position for landing, and switched on his landing lights. Then the lighted runway was coming up to meet them. There was a slight bump. They were down. They were home—safely—from hell!

---

* The code name for the Elsham Wolds airdrome. Each bomber crew also had a code name. That of John's crew was D-Donald.

Under a Cloud

THE CREW OF D-Donald was not happy.

The cause of the unhappiness was the Halifax bomber in which they were flying. The specific reason for their gloominess had developed not long after they had taken part in the raid on Kiel. They had gone on a number of raids after it, and were rapidly gaining the experience that was so vital for survival. Then trouble began.

They had been briefed for a raid on the German city of Mannheim, and were sitting in their plane at the dispersal point ready for their turn to take off. One by one the other bombers had roared down the runway, lifted off, and disappeared into the night sky. But Roper had continued to sit in the cockpit of the plane, revving the motors and discussing with Rose, the engineer, the abnormal reading of the oil and rev (rpm) gauges of the inner starboard, or right, motor. Finally he had shut down the engines and reported to the control tower that because of engine trouble they were not taking off.

The next step was the unpleasant one of reporting to the squadron commander the reason for their failure to take part in the raid. Wing Commander Carter was always annoyed when one of his bombers failed to take off. Sometimes a crew would decide against their better judgment to make a trip rather than risk his displeasure and biting remarks. Roper came away from the interview white faced and tight lipped.

The ground crew responsible for keeping the plane in shape worked painstakingly over the troublesome engine and finally told D-Donald's crew that everything was all right. The next raid, on Nuremberg, went off without any trouble, and the crew thought that the problem had been solved.

But the trouble began again, sometimes with the inner and sometimes the outer motor. Actually, the motors were unpredictable. On occasion everything would work well, and they would take off according to schedule. Then again the plane would sit at its dispersal point and Roper and Rose would rev up the motors, listen to their whine, and watch the fluctuating gauges. Finally Roper would shut down the motors and tell the control tower that their flight was canceled.

His visits with the squadron commander became more and more tense, but he would tell his crew, "Carter can say what he wants to. I'm not taking that kite up with a bad engine." They supported him fully.

The engine trouble continued to hound them through the summer and into the late fall. Slowly they began to drop behind the other planes in the number of bombing flights they were making.

Then an added element made matters worse. Veiled hints were dropped that Roper and his crew were scared and were finding excuses not to go on operations.

One autumn night 103 Squadron was scheduled to take part in an attack on Berlin in which some five hundred planes from a number of squadrons would take part. The name Berlin was one that the bomber crews did not like to hear. Even well-seasoned veterans showed

signs of nervousness when that city was announced as a
target. The reasons were twofold: Not only was the cap-
ital of Germany the most heavily defended of all targets
but also the long flight across enemy territory made the
bombers highly vulnerable. By now John and his crew
had taken part in six raids on Germany and Italy in their
troublesome Halifax.

Instructed from the control tower, plane after plane of
the squadron moved from its dispersal point to take-off
position, thundered down the runway, and disappeared
into the darkness. When Roper's turn came, he again reported he was having trouble with oil pressure and revs,
and asked for a few additional minutes. When the tower
called back, he again asked for more time.

Finally all the planes had taken off, and Roper was
still at the dispersal point revving the troublesome starboard engines and watching the gauges.

Then the control tower spoke again. "The last plane
took off ten minutes ago. Either you take off now, or it
will be too late to go; you'll have to wash out."

Because Roper saw some improvement in the oil pressure, and because of the shadow over him and the crew,
he reported that they were now ready to take off, even
though he did not feel the aircraft was 100 per cent air-
worthy. In order to make up for some of the lost time,
they were instructed not to circle the airdrome to gain
height but to climb en route.

In a few moments they were in the air droning their
way across the dark countryside. John sat in his cubicle
behind the blackout curtain and worked on the chart
glaring white under the angle-poise lamp. The world
outside seemed to fade into unreality. The real world was
his chart with its stark outline of rivers and coasts. Carefully he checked over his flight plan to be sure he had
everything right.

The plan of attack was to approach Berlin from the
north and east. Instructions were to go northeast across

the North Sea, swing around the northern tip of Denmark, and fly south close to the coast of Sweden, down the Kattegat. A continued southern course would bring them east of Berlin, from which direction the attack would be made.

In order to carry a maximum bomb load the fuel reserve was kept down, and bomber crews were instructed that under normal circumstances they were to fly at economical cruising speed to conserve fuel. But this time John, Roper, and Rose, the flight engineer, agreed they would fly at a faster speed in order to make up for lost time. John and Rose kept checking the amount of gasoline left against the flying hours required to get back home.

As they approached Berlin, John stood in his accustomed place behind Rose. With a by now more experienced eye he concluded by the size and extent of the fires burning in the city that they had managed to arrive for the first half of the raid. Berlin was defending itself savagely. A sea of flak was bursting around the raiders, and a solid wall of searchlights surrounded the city.

Gripping his handhold until his knuckles were white, John stared grimly at the searchlights, a sharp ache at the pit of his stomach. How was it possible to get through without being caught in them?

Closer and closer they drew to the wall of light, still continuing the weaving flying pattern. Then suddenly the searchlights parted, leaving a clear path before them as an unfortunate bomber to starboard was coned in the searchlights. Under it the flak mounted, burst, and blossomed like fantastic flowers of death.

About a mile ahead and to port John saw another bomber twist and writhe as it was caught in a large cone of searchlights. With dry, pursed lips he watched the flak exploding all around the plane. Suddenly there was a vivid burst of light, and the doomed bomber plummeted like a fiery comet, to be lost in the flames below. With a shudder John thought, Poor chaps, they didn't have a chance to bail out of that. Automatically he looked at his watch, making a mental note of the time.

The voice of the bomb aimer over the intercom brought his mind back to their plane.

"A bit to the right, Skipper," Toddy was saying as he called for the pilot to fly straight and level for the bombing run.

A shell burst close by, followed by a cannonade like a sharp roll of drums. The plane rocked from side to side.

"That was a near one," Waghorn remarked from his lonely station at the rear. His voice was tight.

John stared at the scene below—the billowing smoke, the hellish flames. Under the glare of another bomber's photoflash he glimpsed for a brief moment streets and buildings. It startled him in spite of himself to see what spoke so clearly of people, men and women like himself, people who loved life and feared death. He made his way back to his cabin, closed the curtains, and turned on the light. In his log he reported the time the unfortunate bomber had gone down.

"Bomb doors open."

Then came the familiar upward leap.

"Bombs gone."

The straight and level course was maintained for a few more seconds until the camera, focused and synchronized to catch the flash of the bursting bombs from about a 14,000-foot altitude, had taken the picture.

As Toddy reported the photo taken and two or three searchlights started swinging ominously toward them, Roper threw the big bomber into strong evasive action to get clear of the target area.

After some minutes his voice came over the intercom, "We're through!" Now the plane settled into that regular weaving pattern that would continue until they were out over the North Sea beyond the range of German night fighters.

Roper now began to fly according to a plan he, John,

and Rose had worked out previously, and which they had used on the last one or two raids. The routine procedure was for the bombers to fly to the target at about 14,000 feet. But when they were well clear of the target area on the way home, they would push the plane's nose down and reduce throttle. In this way they conserved fuel while maintaining speed. But Roper maintained height and did not throttle back. Thus, when the other planes were down to 8,000 or 9,000 feet, theirs was still at 14,000. Then when they were 70 or 80 miles from home John would say, "O.K., Johnny, you can push the nose down now."

With the same amount of throttle on, their speed would go up to about 250 mph as they zoned in in a shallow dive. In this way they would pull ahead of the others.

When they were about halfway across the North Sea, John was able to use his G-box, a radar-type device that enabled him to pinpoint the aircraft's position and make necessary corrections to keep them on course.

As the bomber drew nearer to its base at Elsham Wolds, John would use the G-box with its converging blips on the screen as a homing device. Already he had become so precise in homing in that they would end their approach just to the right of the airdrome and at the right altitude so that the pilot was in the correct position to make the anticlockwise landing circuit. With one circuit they were ready to land and would be the first plane home.

Later on, so regularly were they the first that when the personnel in the control tower heard the faint throbbing of an approaching bomber someone might remark, "Ten shillings that that's Roper. Any takers?" There never were.

Now as they approached Elsham Wolds the station was still in darkness. As soon as the first aircraft received permission to land, the lights of the landing strip would

The girl's voice called, "Hello, D-Donald. This is Bottie. Pancake!"

be turned on and left on until the last plane was in. So John knew that their plane had beat the others.

When John calculated that the airport was coming up on their port side he called to Roper, "O.K., Skipper. Call Bottie."

"Hello, Bottie. Hello, Bottie. D-Donald calling. D-Donald calling. Requesting permission to pancake. Over."

A girl's voice* came to them through the night, "Hello, D-Donald. This is Bottie. Pancake! Pancake! QFE one zero zero five. Over." And the welcome runway lights gleamed in the darkness below.

---

* Women held many responsible jobs during wartime.

Being first in had several advantages, John thought, as they began the swing around the airport. There was no stacking, as was necessary when several planes were ready to land. Stacking meant that when a plane arrived over the station it had to take a flying position 500 feet above the next plane and circle, dropping down 500 feet as plane by plane instructions were received to land. Being stacked also meant that you might circle the station for a half hour waiting your turn.

Then too, the first crew in was always taken straight to debriefing in the lorry. Later arrivals had to wait for another crew to fill the lorry. The first crew was debriefed without any waiting. Again, being first at the mess for a meal meant the cooks would give them extras. Finally, they would get off to bed earlier. Often the first crew was in bed an hour or more before the last ones.

When John's crew entered the debriefing room they sensed at once that something was wrong. Usually the intelligence officer greeted them jovially, with a "Good show, men. Glad to see you back." This time he regarded them silently as they trooped in and sat down.

Then he began to ask questions, not the usual sort of questions asked at a debriefing.

"You fellows were the last up. How long did it take you to make it to the target? What time did you get there?"

Finally he said pointedly, "How come you got home so soon, *if* you have been to the target?"

Roper bristled. "What do you mean, *if?*"

"I might as well be frank with you, gentlemen. You were very late in taking off and yet you are back so early. The next aircraft hasn't arrived yet. There is some doubt as to whether you went to the target at all."

There were exclamations of indignation from the crew.

"Get the photo developed. That will jolly well prove we bombed the target."

"Were you flying straight and level for a good photo?"

"We always fly straight and level for the bombing run."

There was a moment of silence.

"All right. And I'm sorry, gentlemen, but I'm going to have to ask you to wait here until the photo is developed."

A half hour later he called John's crew back into the debriefing room. "We don't understand it, men, but you made it. Your photo is an excellent one, and we have been able to pinpoint it. It shows that you dropped your load two miles east of the center of the target area. You're clear." With a warm handshake to each member of the crew, he apologized for the doubt that had been expressed.

As D-Donald's crew walked to the sergeants' mess they felt that somehow the cloud hovering over them had been rolled back and that this night marked a turning point for them in the squadron.

Riding a Lethal Catherine Wheel

JOHN AND HIS crew were not required to fly on another raid in the troublesome Halifax. Before another operation was called, the whole squadron was ordered to assemble for an important announcement.

Squadron Leader Fox, the senior squadron leader on the station, addressed them. He was lithe and boyish and wore his shapeless officer's cap at a rakish angle. There was a Distinguished Flying Medal ribbon on his battle-dress pocket. He had worked himself up from the ranks and was greatly respected by all the fliers.

"You will be happy to know that we are going to convert shortly to Lancasters," he began.

His words were drowned by an outburst of shouting and cheering.

"We will take delivery of the first aircraft next week, and will have a period of intensive training."

The reason for the popularity of the announcement was clear. In speed, altitude, and performance the Lancaster was greatly superior to the Halifax. The ceiling for the Halifax was about 14,000 feet, the altitude at which flak was worst, it seemed to John. The Lancaster could fly as high as 23,000 feet. Whereas the cruising speed of the Halifax was barely 200 mph, the Lancaster cruised at 260, and if necessary could be pushed along at nearly 300 mph. Also, it lifted more easily from the runway when loaded than the Halifax, and climbed faster. Everyone thought that the heavy losses the squadron had been experiencing would decrease once they were flying Lancasters.

After the squadron was dismissed D-Donald's crew met with big grins on their faces, shaking one another's hands and slapping Roper on the back. "No more engine trouble now, Skipper."

The conversion training of Roper and his crew culminated in a 1,400-mile flight that took them halfway to Iceland and back. This run proved to be a real test of John's skill as a navigator because all the way they were flying over clouds, so that not once during the long flight did they have even a glimpse of land or sea.

Returning to Elsham Wolds they were informed by

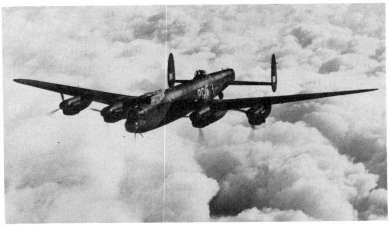

The crews cheered when they converted from Halifaxes to Lancasters.

the control tower that the cloud ceiling was down to 300 feet. With no radar device for blind landings and the balloon barrage of the city of Hull only a few miles to the north, they were directed to another airdrome where the cloud ceiling was higher and where there were no hazards to landing. They had to remain there for two days before the weather permitted them to return to their own field.

With the onset of winter, bombing operations slowed down. Sometimes two weeks would go by without a raid being carried out. But whenever the weather cleared, operations were scheduled against the enemy. Slowly the number of raids John and his crew made grew.

The latter half of January, 1943, saw operations at a standstill because of bad weather blanketing England and Europe. But on January 30 the weather cleared and a raid was scheduled against the industrial city of Hamburg. It was to be John's thirteenth raid.

A strong wind was blowing at a 25 to 30 degree angle across the runway. The pilots had been warned that they would need to carefully handle their planes, heavily loaded with a 4,000-pound blockbuster and another 4,000 pounds of small incendiary bombs.

Roper sat in his cabin checking over his engines. Rose sat in his usual place, on the top step leading down to Todd's compartment, handling the four throttles under Roper's direction.

Finally they were instructed to take off. Roper released the brakes, and the plane began to pick up speed down the runway.

Standing in his usual take-off position, John saw that the wind was nudging them to port.

"More port, less starboard," Roper instructed Rose.

By now they were rolling at 40 to 50 mph.

"More port! Less starboard!" Roper said sharply as Rose failed to respond quickly.

The aircraft was traveling fast enough to be blown by

The plane roared diagonally across the runway toward the chalk pit.

the cross wind but not enough to respond to the rudder, and was now swinging to the left about 15 degrees.

"Reduce starboard!" Roper knocked Rose's hand from the throttles and took over.

Now the plane was off the lighted concrete runway, roaring diagonally away at some 60 to 70 mph, its landing lights surging across the grassy field.

Adjusting the throttle swiftly, Roper managed to swing the craft around on the grass, parallel to the runway.

Ahead where the runway ended was a 40-to-50-foot-deep chalk pit. Roper had to make a split-second life-or-death decision. Should he throttle down and try to stop, perhaps with the result that they would end up with a tremendous explosion in the chalk pit? Or should he endeavor to take off blind without the lights of the runway to guide him.

He chose the latter course, and eased the throttles forward until the plane was traveling about 80 mph and responding to rudder control. Then with a swift motion he pushed the four throttle levers "through the gate" for the extra power available for take-off. Immediately the two starboard motors died.

From the control tower the flight controllers watched each shadowy plane thunder down the runway, probing ahead with its take-off lights, lift off, and then vanish into the night as its lights were switched off.

When D-Donald's turn came it became apparent as the plane gathered speed down the runway that something was wrong. They saw it drift too far to the left of the runway. They saw it gather speed, stray from the runway, and roar off into the field.

Then with relief they saw the craft straighten out and gather speed for take-off.

But suddenly the plane swung around violently. In frozen fascination they saw one of the bouncing landing lights drop toward the ground while the other swung upward. The bomber spun wildly, crossing the runway at a 90-degree angle. The landing gear on one side of the plane had collapsed, causing the wing tip to dig into the ground, sending the aircraft spinning across the airfield.

"Down on the floor!" someone shouted. If the blockbuster aboard the gyrating plane exploded, the control tower and a lot of other buildings on the station would be demolished; and a lot of people with them.

John hung on for grim life as the plane careened to starboard and bounced crabwise across the runway. There was a rending and tearing underneath him. A sickening downward plunge of the fuselage told him that part of the undercarriage had collapsed. Then he was thrown violently against the side of the aircraft as the starboard wing slashed into the ground. Like a giant Catherine wheel the plane gyrated across the field.

In a spasm of crunches and rendings, the bucking craft lurched to a halt.

Momentarily dazed, John was aware that the port engines were still running, although Roper had managed to cut them back. Around him swirled the pungent fumes of gasoline. The two starboard engines had been torn from the wing, leaving gaping holes. High-octane fuel spurted from the tanks in the wing like a fountain. And

4

eight thousand pounds of bombs in the bomb bay! One
spark from those engines could trigger a blast that would
atomize D-Donald's crew and demolish much of the
airport.

The Rolls Royce Merlin engines added to the critical-
ness of the situation. The moment they were shut off they
had the nasty habit of belching flames from the exhausts.
But to leave them running would be fatal. Roper cut the
motors.

John heard the cough as they spat and died. He tensed
for the explosion. But no explosion came; only an eerie
silence. But the very hot engines could still set off the
swirling gasoline fumes. The crew did not wait to see.
Ripping open the escape hatch above the pilot's seat,
John pulled himself up through it closely followed by
Roper and Rose. They slid down the fuselage onto the
wing, then dropped to the ground. The other crew members had jumped clear of the plane through other escape
hatches.

With Roper and Rose just behind him and the other
crew members running ahead, John raced away from the
lethal, broken craft, waiting all the time for the blast that
would swallow him. But all he heard was the sound of
planes droning overhead, his own labored breathing, and
the thud of feet on grass.

Finally they realized that the plane was not going to
catch fire. Slowly they returned to the aircraft. The
damage was appalling.

No one could understand why the gas hadn't exploded.

An International Incident

KIEL. DUISBURG. BREMEN. Berlin. Wilhelmshaven. Nuremberg. Lorient. Munich. Stuttgart. Turin. Milan. Saint-Nazaire. Cologne. Mannheim. Essen. Düsseldorf.

A few days after their ground crash John's crew was issued a new Lancaster and they entered the ever-intensifying operations against the enemy. Each raid was represented by a bomb painted on the nose of the plane. Slowly at first but now more rapidly the symbolic bombs grew in number. Whether they would ever reach the magic number of thirty was the question in the mind of every man. When thirty raids were completed the first tour of duty was done. The crew that finished a tour would be given a lengthy period of rest before beginning a second but shorter tour of twenty-five operations. After a second tour a crew was regarded as having fulfilled its duty, looked death in the face often enough.

But the grim fact was that by the time John and his crew joined 103 Squadron, few crews were getting to paint the

As the war intensified, the cities of Europe withered under the bombs.

thirtieth bomb on their plane. With unnerving frequency old faces disappeared from the squadron. New faces appeared. But sometimes they were glimpsed only once or twice during a briefing, and then not seen again.

Not infrequently crews hardly had time to unpack their kits before they were lost. Sometimes on the squadron's notice board under the heading "New Arrivals," seven names would be listed. Under "Missing in Action" would be the same seven names.

Of the fifteen crews senior to John's when he joined the squadron, only one completed thirty raids. Two were transferred elsewhere; the other twelve were lost. In addition, during the six months John spent with the squadron some twenty crews that joined after he did were lost. .A similar situation applied to bomber squadrons in other parts of Britain. It has been estimated that of all the men who flew as bomber command air crews, fully seventy per cent lost their lives in action.

In time many at Elsham Wolds began to feel that none of the crews of 103 Squadron would be able to get to thirty operations. Months had passed since a crew had succeeded in reaching that elusive number. Many did not even reach ten.

Thus each trip was filled with the terrible drama of life and death. But although it became almost routine, one could never get used to it anymore than he could get used to physical torture. Every man of a bomber crew lived under a stress that was seldom, if ever, absent. Even when he was away from his squadron on rest leave, somewhere in the back of his mind lurked the knowledge that in a few days—five, three, two—he would once again be flying over Germany. And perhaps flying beside him this time would be the angel of death who would reach out and touch his craft with a deadly touch.

Each man tried to hide these thoughts and feelings in his own way. But behind no matter what kind of mask he endeavored to conceal his real feelings, occasionally the mask would slip, revealing, if but for a moment, by a word or a look in the eyes, the fear, the strain, underneath.

Actually, not all operations were regarded as equally dangerous. Some cities were defended more lightly and less efficiently than others. Raids on the Italian cities of Milan and Turin were regarded as being so relatively hazardless that they were recorded on the planes' noses not by bombs but by ice-cream cones.

It was on one of these raids that the Royal Air Force bomber group triggered an international incident, and John's crew had their only contact with a German night fighter.

The target that night was Milan. During briefing the navigators were instructed that the route was to be south across France, skirting the western border of neutral Switzerland. They were to take their directions from the Pathfinder Squadrons. These squadrons were made up of seasoned crews flying in planes fitted with special radar-type equipment for accurate navigation. It was the work of the planes of these squadrons to fly ahead of the bombers and pinpoint the target for each raid. This was done by dropping great marker flares that burned long and brightly on the target. On this particular occasion they were also to drop flares at a specified point southwest of Switzerland. This was to be the marker signal at which the bombers were to turn east on a course that would take them over some lower Alpine peaks to Milan.

For three uneventful hours D-Donald droned south across England, the English Channel, and France. Then they saw the flares. Taking his position from them, John gave Roper his course east, but in ten or fifteen minutes it became apparent that something had gone wrong. For below them was not a countryside unilluminated except for a full moon shining on the snow telling them they were flying over Italy. Instead, they saw houses and villages fully lighted, and a train with carriage windows gleaming brightly rolling along beneath. They were over Switzerland.

After consulting his chart and rechecking his calculations, John concluded that the Pathfinder's navigators had made a mistake. The planes were bucking a stronger wind than they had realized. Consequently, the Pathfinders were not as far south as they should have been when they dropped their flares, which had signaled a turn before it should have been made.

Quickly John and Roper consulted together. What should they do? There were two choices. They could fly back and go south to where they should have turned. Or they could look for a low pass that would take them across the higher Swiss Alps to Italy. (Flying over the higher peaks of the Alps was impossible because of the weight of their bomb load.) The first was quickly ruled out; there was too great a chance that they would not have enough fuel to take them back home after such a detour. Moreover, they would then be going against the stream of bombers that would be flying in an easterly direction north of the range. They opted for the second alternative.

Getting out his topographical maps, John looked through the windows of the pilot's cabin at the mountainous peaks to starboard, gleaming calm and white in the bright moonlight.

Noting the shape and position of each peak and carefully scanning the elevations indicated on his map, he finally was able to pinpoint their position.

With this information at hand, Roper swung the plane southward. Ahead and above them loomed the cold, inscrutable peaks.

"Say, Skipper, those look like pretty solid clouds ahead. I hope you don't plan to fly through them," remarked Smith from the mid-upper gun turret.

"You should worry, you're at the rear of this crate," retorted Toddy at his guns in the front turret. "If we fly into them, I'll be there first."

As they neared the mountains the pass John was looking for came into view. Banking around, then leveling
off, Roper flew the heavily laden plane into it. On either
side the white peaks rose above them. Underneath they
did not have much leeway. As John watched the plane's
shadow flitting across the snow below, it seemed that
sometimes there were only feet to spare. But at last the
ground began to drop away. They were through. In a
short time they dropped their bombs on Milan and turned
toward home. Tomorrow the Swiss would formally com-
plain to the British Government regarding the violation
of international law, and the British would make an apol-
ogy.

Three hours later they were flying over the north of
France, approaching the English Channel. Suddenly
Waghorn, the rear gunner, reported, "Bandit [enemy
plane] about thirty degrees to starboard."

"Is he attacking?" Roper asked.

"No, he's not coming at us. He's cutting across our
tail to port."

"Can you definitely get him?"

"He's not close enough for me to be dead sure."

"I've got my guns on him, too," Smith reported. "I
agree with Waggy. He's not close enough."

"Then don't try to get him. He may not have seen us,
so there's no use taking chances."

John made his way to the pilot's cabin and looked
out. By now the other plane, a Messerschmitt-109, had
changed position somewhat, and was flying parallel with
them. He *had* seen them.

All guns trained on the fighter, flying just out of range
for a sure hit, D-Donald's crew waited tensely for the
attack. Roper instructed John and Dobie, the wireless
operator, to check carefully in all directions around the
plane. This could be a decoy, taking up their attention
while another attacked.

For several seconds the Messerschmitt flew along

with them, then banked off in a turning dive. For two or three minutes all in the bomber watched, straining their eyes for the shadowy enemy that might attack suddenly from above or below. But the seconds ticked off. Apparently the night fighter pilot had decided to leave them alone.

As they continued toward home the crew speculated why they were not attacked. They concluded that the German must have run out of ammunition.

It was not until after the war that John discovered that German night fighters were not at all eager to tackle a Lancaster. One of the most successful German night fighter pilots admitted that once his plane had been seen and the gunners started shooting, he left them alone and went off in search of a less-alert target.

The Last Raid

FEBRUARY, 1943, WAS a month of great activity for the Royal Air Force bomber command and, consequently, for 103 Squadron. Pressure on Germany was being increased, and as a result the bombings had been stepped up. This meant that crews were going on raids more frequently than usual.

It also meant increased losses for bomber command. From almost every raid one crew and sometimes two of 103 Squadron failed to return. With such losses, the squadron soon would be wiped out.

Under the circumstances the strain on the air crews was extreme. Occasionally a man would reach the place where he could no longer stand the strain. Rather than go on he would refuse to fly, and therefore face the disgrace of being charged with lack of moral fiber.

March 9. John's crew had been on five raids in seven nights, and tonight they were listed to go again. The target was Munich. This would be their twenty-fifth.

They had had a stand-down two nights

Five raids in seven nights—and John's crew was listed to go again.

before. But now as they sat around on their parachute packs at the dispersal point near their plane it was obvious that they were very tired. Pilot Officer Henderson, one of the squadron's doctors, drove up in his car and climbed out. Two or three of the crew were holding their heads in their hands.

The doctor looked around at the men in silence for a moment.

"You fellows are a bit tired, aren't you?"

"Who wouldn't be, Doc? Five ops in seven nights."

"Do you think you ought to go tonight? I could stand you down as being unfit."

"No, we're having too good a run, Doc. Let's not break it. Let's get it over with."

For a few moments the doctor stood there weighing the situation. He was uncertain what to do. Reluctantly he said, "O.K. If you want to go, we'll let you. Good luck!"

He walked slowly to his car, climbed in, and drove off.

Tonight John had taken several caffeine tablets to keep awake, but even so he had to fight to keep his eyes open.

After what seemed to be multiplied nights of endless

hours, endless throbbing motors, endless weaving, he saw the Pathfinders' white marker flares go off to port, indicating the turning point for the final run to Munich.

The markers told John that they were several miles off track to the southwest, blown there by a stronger wind than they had anticipated. Instructing Roper to fly visually to the markers, John made a careful note of the time they altered course and the new compass heading. This information would be essential for working out the correct wind for the return journey.

Making a fix from the markers, John gave Roper the flight-plan course for the target. He then tried to work out the wind velocity to calculate the correct course for home. But he found himself staring blankly at the Mercator's projection, his mind refusing to work. Deciding to make the calculations after they had dropped their bombs, he left his desk and stood behind Rose, looking for the first signs of the target.

At last he saw the familiar red Pathfinder marker flares bursting over the target some miles ahead. They fell to the ground and burned blood red, each like an exposed heart.

They approached an inferno of streets, houses, factories, and hospitals. Around them the flak exploded in savage bursts of yellow, orange, and red.

Then suddenly it was no longer night. It was day with a light that day never had. The city, the sky, the swarm of attacking planes, etched upon John's mind in a terrible brightness. In his twenty-four previous operations John had never seen such a massive explosion. Then it was dark again.

"Log that explosion, Navigator," Roper was saying. "That might have been a gas works. Or a mine dump."

"Bombs away."

The plane leaped up and held its course for a few seconds. Then came the flash that told that the photo had been taken. At the same moment they banked and swung away from the holocaust beneath that was Munich.

Settling himself heavily in his seat in his navigator's compartment, John pulled the curtains closed, switched on his angle-poise lamp, wrote in his log the details of the explosion they had seen, and noted when the bombs were dropped.

He had given Roper the flight-plan course for the homeward journey. Now he tried to concentrate on working out the speed and direction of the wind that had blown them off track on the way to Munich. It was vital to have this information if they were to make the proper adjustments to keep from being blown off course on their way home. With painful slowness he forced his mind to make the calculations.

A half hour passed after the dropping of the bombs before John was able to complete his work. Now, having all the information required, he tried to figure out their course for home. But his mind refused to work. Dully he wondered whether the caffeine he had taken was drugging his mind instead of keeping him awake. He had heard that it worked that way for some people.

The motors hummed on monotonously, hypnotically. Then slowly their sound faded, was silent. John's head sank down onto his chart. He was asleep.

A sudden crash jolted him wide awake. They had been hit by an ack-ack shell!

Quickly John snapped on his parachute and stepped into the pilot's cabin.

"Can you see what the damage is?" Roper asked tersely. He nodded toward the starboard side of the plane.

John peered through the plexiglass canopy. He saw flames dancing round a hole in the wing. "We're on fire!"

"Push the extinguisher button," Roper ordered.

But the fire did not go out. It became worse.

Then ominous bangings began in the burning wing. The aileron controls jerked in Roper's hands. The plane was out of control.

Knowing they must bail out immediately, John worked desperately to buckle Roper into his parachute.

Before he could do so the burning plane flipped over and began spiraling toward earth, binding John to the floor with centrifugal force.

Suddenly there was a crashing explosion and a burst of cosmic light, and oblivion swallowed him.

From the depths of an infinite blackness a great misty, red-glowing mass emerged, swept across John's consciousness, and disappeared, to be followed by another, and another, and another.

Slowly the haze drifted from his mind and his sight cleared. He was falling over and over backwards through space. The recurring burning mass that was moving across his vision was his plane as it plunged, a fiery comet, toward the earth.

Totally conscious now, John reached with his right hand for the parachute strapped to his chest, and groped for the ripcord ring that would release it. A terrible fear gripped him. The ring was not there.

Looking at his chest in the faint moonlight as he fell he saw to his immense relief that he had clipped his parachute on as for a left-handed person. Reaching across his chest, he gripped the ring at his left side with his right hand and pushed it out.

The pack burst open in front of his face, and his parachute billowed above his head. Then there was a jerk, and he looked up to see the most beautiful sight in the world—the white circular canopy swinging above him.

Below him and off to his right the glowing comet that was D-Donald was streaking for the ground. Then it burst like a fiery fountain and disappeared except for a few glowing embers.

John peered around him in the moonlight looking for another parachute. Was it possible that others of the crew had survived? But he could see nothing.

Now he began to take stock of his situation. Was he wounded? Cautiously he began to examine his head, his legs, his arms. His flying helmet was gone, but he could find no sign of any cut on his head. His left shoe was missing, which was going to prove to be a great inconvenience. Later he discovered a small triangular tear in his tunic and another small tear in one of his trouser legs.

He became conscious that his parachute harness was cutting into his legs. Gripping the shrouds he pulled upward in an effort to shift the harness straps a little. The action pulled him into a sitting position. He was still struggling to find a more comfortable position when unexpectedly he received a painful jarring blow from beneath. He had come down hard upon a railway track. His parachute settled down beside him.

Climbing painfully to his feet, he quickly removed the parachute and harness and gathered everything up, looking around all the while for some place to hide it. It would not do to leave it there as evidence of his landing.

The track was built on a small embankment. Below was a thicket of trees. He ran down the embankment, threw down his parachute among the trees, raked together some leaves and twigs and covered the incriminating whiteness. He glanced at his luminous watch. It said one-thirty.

Then he became conscious of shouting some distance away. His parachute had been seen descending in the moonlight. He was in occupied France. Would it be friendly Frenchmen or Germans who were approaching? He decided that it had to be Germans. Under the circumstances the French would approach secretively. Somehow he had to get away fast.

Then another sound caught his attention. The chugging of a slow-moving train laboring up an incline. Here was a promise of escape. Tensely he waited among the trees as the sound of the voices came closer. It was touch-and-go whether the train or his searchers would reach him first.

The chugging of the train became louder. Then the dark shape of an unlighted engine loomed out of the night.

John waited behind a tree for the engine to pass, then raced up the embankment and ran as fast as he could alongside the train. The hard stones hurt his shoeless foot. And the train was moving faster than he could run. But he just had to get aboard that train!

An open wagon was moving past him, its top just above eye level. Desperately he flung himself at it and grasped the edge. The speed of the train pulled him off his feet. Horror swept over him. For a moment he thought he would be swung under the wheels. But then somehow he got a foothold, clawed his way over the side, and fell panting inside the wagon.

He found himself lying on top of bales of hay. As soon as he caught his breath he began to shift them around so that he could lie comfortably in the center, yet without easily being seen.

The freight train picked up speed. With a tremendous sense of relief John noted that it was traveling westward. That way lay England. And even though many miles of country and multitudes of imponderables were between them, he was going to try to get back there.

Now that he was safe, at least for the time being, his whole being cried out for sleep. But he couldn't sleep. Not just yet.

From his pocket he took his survival kit. Inside were silk maps covering the whole of Europe showing major roads, railways, towns, and large villages. In addition were large sums of French and German currency, a tiny compass, a five-inch-long hacksaw blade, highly concentrated food tablets, and pills for purifying water.

John had added to this Air Force issue a small penknife.

With the penknife he now began to remove from his battle dress all insignia and buttons that would give him away. These he tossed outside the wagon one by one as the train rolled along. The only remaining means of identity was his Air Force identity disk.

As he worked he began to think of the experience through which he had just passed. Probably less than fifteen minutes had elapsed since he had been awakened by the explosion of the ack-ack shell hitting the wing of the plane. It was difficult for him to realize all that had happened in that brief period.

He thought of his companions. Had any of them been as lucky as he, and survived? The memory of the plane's fiery trail through the sky and the explosion as it hit the ground seemed to offer little hope that anyone had.

But why had *he* come through alive, and almost without a scratch? He could find no answer to the question.

Having finished his task, he found a comfortable position lying between the bales of hay and permitted nature to assert herself. In a moment he was fast asleep.

The clock hands in the control tower at Elsham Wolds moved slowly toward 2:30 A.M. The controllers, who had been sitting around sleepily, became more alert. It was time for the first planes to arrive.

In a few minutes the faint familiar drone of an approaching Lancaster came through the night. Then a voice crackled over the speakers.

"Hello, Bottie. Hello, Bottie. G-George calling. G-George calling. Requesting permission to pancake. Over."

The people in the control room looked at one another, an unspoken question on their lips.

"For You the War Is Over"

THE JERKING AND clattering of the train as it came to a stop awakened John. Dawn was just beginning to break, and a sharp chill was in the air. He was glad for the white turtle-neck sweater under his battle dress. His watch said five-fifty.

Stiffly he moved his limbs, then cautiously pushed his head above the edge of the wagon and looked around. Several tracks ran beside the train. Off to the side, lines of railway cars stood silently. He was either in a marshaling yard or at a major station or terminal.

Just then a sign caught his eye: Reims.

Seven or eight carriages ahead an overhead footbridge crossed the track. It was unused at the moment, but anyone crossing it had but to glance in his direction to see him. The bales of hay were arranged in such a way that he could not move them to hide himself completely.

A movement caught his eye. A workman was crossing the bridge. Tensely, John waited for the man to glance in his direction. But he kept on, looking straight ahead.

Clearly, John couldn't stay where

he was. After glancing around to see whether anyone was in sight he dropped over the side of the car and began to walk along the tracks. He hoped he was on the south side of Reims. His goal was to get to neutral Spain, from which he was confident he could reach England. Spain was several hundred miles southwest of Reims, but he was jolly well going to make the effort to get there.

Cutting across several railway tracks, he finally came to a cobbled road, on each side of which were large buildings he judged to be warehouses. The road was going in the general direction he wanted to travel, so he decided to stay on it.

He soon realized that he was indeed on the southern outskirts of Reims. To his right beyond the rows of carriages lining the tracks and the railway buildings he could see the city, with here and there a cathedral spire rising above the other buildings.

As he trudged along, the buildings on the south side of the road became fewer. Then came a heavy wire mesh fence enclosing a large open field. Beyond that, to the south, was more or less open rolling country, made up of what appeared to be vineyards. But he could see no road going that direction.

By now he had walked about a mile. There were getting to be a few people about on their way to work. Two or three of them looked curiously at the young lad walking along with only one shoe. John began to get edgy. Somehow he was going to have to find a place to hide for the day, and travel at night.

Finally he came to a narrow canal running north and south. A small arched footbridge crossed it to some houses. A towpath ran along the side of the canal on the other side.

Crossing the bridge, John turned south on the towpath. Close to the towpath on his right a seven-foot-high wooden fence extended for some 250 feet. Coming to the end of the fence, he glanced around quickly to be sure no one was observing him, grasped the top of the fence, pulled himself up, and looked over.

Inside was a large garden, which he saw at once would be an ideal place to hide. A house at the far end of the yard was separated from his end by a high hedge, several fruit trees, and some grapevines, which effectually hid his area of the yard from the house. At his end of the garden about twenty feet away was a large shed.

Quickly clambering over the fence, John dropped to the ground and made himself as unobtrusive as possible. No sign or sound from the house indicated that he had been seen.

Getting out his maps, he found one of France. It showed only the major roads. He decided it would not be safe to follow them. The best thing to do would be to follow the canal south until he came to a road. Épernay was the next town of any size. He would head in that direction.

By now his stomach was demanding food in no uncertain manner. He had not eaten a full meal since the early afternoon of the previous day. But all the food he had was the concentrated food tablets. Eating one of these, he lay on the ground on his stomach and began to doze off.

Sleep had almost claimed him when he heard a dog whining nearby. For a moment John did not move. Then very slowly he turned his head and looked with half-closed eyes in the direction from which the sound was coming. Standing looking at him from about twenty feet away was a mongrel wire-haired terrier.

If I make eye contact with him he may start to bark, John thought. He kept on watching the dog with his eyes half closed. Finally the dog left. But several times through the day it returned, stood at about the same place for four or five minutes, and whined. John feared each time that it would bark and cause someone to investigate.

As the time drew on toward sunset, John began to feel

restless. He had slept quite a lot through the day in spite of his hunger, and now he was eager to be on his way.

Cautiously he gazed around, while still lying on the ground. The dog was nowhere in sight. He got up, went to the fence, pulled himself up, and looked over. Two or three people were walking along the road on the other side of the canal. He waited a few moments, and checked again. This time all was clear.

Quickly he climbed the fence, dropped onto the towpath, and began to walk south. After he had gone about a quarter of a mile he came to a small gravel road leading west through relatively flat treeless country. A quarter of a mile along this road, and he found another crossing it, going in a north-south direction. He turned south.

By now it was dark, except for the stars. The moon would not be up for several hours.

John's unshod foot was beginning to give him trouble. He stopped, removed the sock from his right foot and pulled it over the left. Then he walked on with only his shoe on his right foot. In spite of the two socks, his left foot began to bother him more and more. A sense of desperation began to take hold of him. If only he could get something for his foot—and food for his clamoring stomach.

Several times he came to branching roads. Each time he took his bearings by the stars and turned on the road leading most directly south.

About one o'clock he found himself approaching some houses. As he continued he saw that he was entering a village. He stopped for a few moments in uncertainty. He did not want to pass through, but decided that he had no choice.

He now realized that he was in a small village built around an open square. Just then a dog began to bark somewhere inside a house. Then another joined it, and another. In a moment it seemed one hundred dogs were barking furiously. Fortunately, all were inside houses.

Anxiously he looked around, trying to decide what to do. With all of the barking, someone was bound to investigate.

In the center of the square he saw a large monument, probably a memorial of World War I. Quickly he ran and stood in its shadow. Hardly had he gotten to it when the whole square was bathed in light from a battery of spotlights erected on a building on the south side. John stood as though paralyzed. All was up. He was discovered!

Then he realized that he was standing on the north side of the monument in the only place in the square shaded from the lights.

Like one of the statues, he stood stone still feeling as though a hundred pairs of eyes were probing every shadow searching for him. The dogs continued barking. But nobody came into the square.

Gradually the dogs quieted down, but still the lights remained on. One minute, two minutes, three minutes passed. Then abruptly the lights went off.

John froze where he was several more minutes, expecting that momentarily the lights would blaze on again. Then he hurried across the square and away from the village.

Now he walked through a wooded area. Time began to drag. His foot hurt, but he forced himself to limp on.

It began to get colder. He wasn't dressed to be outside through a night in early spring. The chill began to penetrate. He began to realize that he had to find help soon or he would not be able to go on.

About an hour before dawn the woods on the right of the road gave way to open farmland. About a hundred and fifty yards ahead he could see the outline of a lone house set back from the road. Feeling desperate, John decided to seek help there. A wooden fence stood between him and the house. He found the gate and started to open it, then hesitated. Suppose the people were not friendly?

He lifted the wooden bar on the gate, went through, and closed the gate behind him. Going to the door he raised his hand to knock. Again he hesitated. Should he do it?

Making up his mind, he knocked. The sound echoed inside, but no sign came that anyone had heard.

He knocked again, harder. A dog began to bark inside. Then a light came on in an upstairs room. Its rays made a patch of light in the yard. John moved back so that he stood in the light and could be seen.

Soon a light came on downstairs. Then the door opened and the outline of a burly man filled the door.

John remained in the light from the upstairs room.

Not being able to speak French, he said, "R.A.F."

The man began to speak rapidly and excitedly and raised his hand above his head. Something in his hand glinted in the light—a long dagger.

John spoke again, in pleading tones, "R.A.F! English!"

Still holding his hand with the dagger above his head, the man began to shout.

John couldn't understand his words, but his tones and actions were eloquent. John turned and walked toward the gate. As he closed it he looked back. The man was still standing with hand upraised.

Turning away, John continued down the road.

Gradually the dawn crept in. Feeling quite miserable, he hobbled on.

Another hour passed. A bit of the chill began to leave the air as the sun came up, dappling the road through the trees.

A house came in sight down the road. Then several houses. He was nearing another village.

The first house was standing about one hundred feet from the road in an unfenced field. He decided that he was going to have to take a chance and call at that house, for the farther he went into the village the more likely it

A French village, typical of the ones John passed through as a fugitive.

was that a number of people would see him, even at that
early hour. But it was imperative that the only ones to see
him would be those who would—he hoped—help. If he
were caught he would be treated as a prisoner of war. But
a Frenchman discovered by the Germans to be aiding the
enemy would, without doubt, receive harsh treatment.
He almost certainly would be executed.

Earnestly hoping that the people in the house would
be sympathetic and willing to help, he cut across the field
until he was within a few yards of the house. A mound of
earth offered some cover while he looked the situation

over, so he lay on his stomach facing the house and waited.

In a few moments a woman of about thirty came out of the back door and went to a shed behind the house. When she came out John raised himself a bit and called out, "R.A.F."

Startled, the woman looked in his direction, then hurried into the house.

After a while a tall, friendly looking man came out and walked toward John. John got to his feet, pointed to the sky and repeated, "R.A.F."

Nodding pleasantly, the man signaled John to follow him. But instead of going toward the house, he started down the path toward the village.

Stopping, John pointed to the sky, again saying urgently, "R.A.F." Then he indicated by signals that he did not want to go to the village. But smilingly his guide continued to beckon.

John knew now that the man planned to turn him over to the Germans, otherwise he would have taken him inside the house at once. Feeling that he had been betrayed but too exhausted to resist he slowly followed.

As he trudged silently behind his captor—because essentially that was what the man was—John noted that the village was small, with perhaps twenty neat stone houses with steep slate roofs fronting a single street. At the end of the curving street was a small church with a little belfry.

About fifty yards down the road they stopped at a house on the left side of the street. The man knocked and without waiting for someone to open the door walked in, signaling for John to follow.

John found himself in a small, simply furnished parlor. His guide talked in French to a smiling middle-aged couple, making occasional gestures toward him.

After a few moments of conversation the woman motioned for John to follow her into the next room. Her husband followed. This room, larger than the first, contained an unpretentious settee, some chairs, and several small pictures on the wall.

The man pointed to a chair. John sat down then, smiling, pointed at his shoeless left foot.

After the man and woman had talked together briefly, the woman left the house. In less than five minutes she was back with an old shoe, which she handed to John. It didn't match John's regulation shoe very well, and it needed polishing, but John accepted it eagerly. He tried it on. It was a little tight across the instep, but otherwise it fitted fine.

The shoe had a remarkable effect on John's morale. Immediately he felt capable of facing the world again. He had not realized how much the loss of his shoe had affected him.

But it would take more than morale to get him back to England. Some forty hours had passed since he had eaten, and he had not had satisfactory sleep for two nights. Consequently, he was feeling almost totally exhausted. He indicated that he was hungry. The woman disappeared into the other room, while the two men stood watching him and talking to each other.

Soon the woman returned with a plate on which were a thick slab of dark rye bread, a large piece of red sausage, and a glass of red wine. She set it on a small table in front of John's chair.

John smiled his appreciation, and ate ravenously.

When he was finished, one of the men took the plate, pointed to the settee, and said, "Sleep," in English.

Then he went out and closed the door, leaving John alone. John stretched himself on the settee, which was set about two feet from the wall, and was immediately asleep.

The sound of voices awakened him. For a moment he could not recall where he was. Then he looked around.

The door was open. A chair had been set in the doorway at right angles to the frame. Sitting on it with his left foot in John's room and his right in the other was a man about fifty years of age in the uniform of a gendarme. He was talking quietly to the people in the other room who were out of John's sight. In one hand the gendarme was holding a piece of bread; in the other was a glass of wine. At his side was his revolver in a holster.

Their eyes met. The gendarme smiled. John detected a look of sympathy in the smile.

John swung his legs to the floor and sat up. The gendarme stood up and came into the room.

"Preezener," he said. "Tel-e-phone Feld Gendarme."

He made a motion indicating that German military police would be coming to pick John up. Then he signaled that John should sleep some more.

Shrugging his shoulders, John held out his hands in a gesture of resignation. Yawning, he glanced at his watch. It was ten o'clock. He turned on the couch to lie down. As he did so, he noticed the window behind the settee. It was made in two halves. The bottom part had been pushed up so that the lower part of the window was wide open.

Closing his eyes, and pretending to try to sleep, John began to ponder the implications of the open window. How strange that it is open, he thought. I'm supposed to be a prisoner here.

He continued to think about the open window. It was about five feet behind him. It would take only a second to get through it if he could catch the gendarme when his attention was focused on something else. Lying on his side, he began to watch through half-closed eyes. The gendarme was once again in conversation with the people in the other room, who apparently were seated at a table.

About five minutes passed. The conversation had become animated. The gendarme was leaning forward in his chair, his face toward those in the other room.

John leaped from the settee, covered the few feet in a stride and vaulted through the window.

Then he discovered why the window might have been left open. The house was built on an incline so that while the front was level with the street, the back was a story high.

Fortunately the ground below the window was soft. As he landed he broke into a run.

The gendarme did not follow him through the window but ran out the door and around the house. By the time he got to the back of the house John was some seventy-five yards away racing across open land.

Glancing over his shoulder he saw that the gendarme was running after him, his revolver in his hand. Then he heard a shot.

John was really not too worried about the revolver. He had learned during pistol practice while at basic training that there is very little chance of hitting a moving object at a range of seventy-five yards when you yourself are moving.

The gendarme continued to shoot. John counted the shots. Five, six. That ends his bullets, John thought.

Ahead about three quarters of a mile to the left was a forest. If he could make it there, he might be able to get away.

Then he saw a barbed-wire fence just a few yards in front of him, running at an angle between him and the forest. If he tried to get through the fence the gendarme would catch up with him. He was forced to veer to the left and follow the line of the fence. And the fence continued for about 150 yards, right back to the road.

Standing resolutely in the road was a French boy about sixteen years of age. Held threateningly in his hand was a big dagger. A scared but determined look was on his face.

John was too winded to tackle him or to try to get past. He paused, and the two stood facing each other while John got his breath back.

As John stood there breathing heavily he heard the

sound of a motor. Then around the curve of the road a green car appeared and came to a stop with a squeal of brakes a few feet away. Inside John could see some men in the green uniforms of the German Wehrmacht.

The boy began to talk excitedly to them in German. In a moment two or three pistols were pointing at John through the car's windows. John put up his hands. Just at that moment the gendarme came puffing up.

Then the car doors opened and three soldiers in their twenties got out. One of them walked behind John and frisked him. Satisfied that he was not armed he spoke in English, "For you the war is over."

The words affected John as though a bucket of icy water had been thrown over him. Up to that moment, even when he had been seeking to escape from enemy-controlled territory, the war had not been actually real to him. But now he realized that he was face to face with the enemy—in enemy hands. But he determined grimly, For me the war is *not* over!

With John sitting beside the driver and the other two in the back, the car turned toward Reims.

Midnight Escape

IN ABOUT THREE quarters of an hour they arrived at Reims. After driving for several blocks and making two or three turns they came to what seemed to be a prison. John was taken into a fairly large building and led to a cell. The door slammed shut, and the key was turned.

John was surprised that he had not been searched thoroughly before being locked up. He still had all of his escape equipment.

Rapidly he set about hiding it. His German jailer might come back at any moment and search him.

Removing his trousers, he used his penknife to open the stitching in the waistband. Then he folded the maps in narrow, flat strips and carefully worked them into the folds. He concealed the button-sized compass in the same manner. For a moment he thought of hiding some of the money. But the realization that the paper would crackle and give it away to searchers made him decide against it. Besides, if they found the money they might search more thoroughly. He decided to leave it in his pockets.

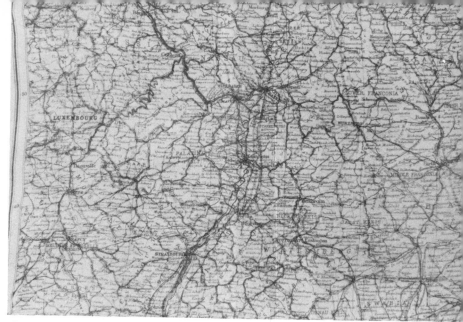

The actual silk maps of Europe which John concealed from his captors.

He took off one of his socks, put the hacksaw under his foot, and put the sock back on. The bare blade did not feel too comfortable when he put his shoe back on, but the discomfort would be worth while if he could get away with it. Then he sat on the wooden bench that was the only piece of furniture in the cell and waited to see what would happen next.

In about an hour he heard the key turning in the lock. The door opened and two German guards came in. One of them was carrying a metal tray containing a knife and fork, a tin cup filled with ersatz (synthetic) coffee, a piece of rye bread, a small pat of margarine, and a red sausage like the one he had had for breakfast. He set the tray down on the bench.

Then one of them searched John, taking from his pockets the money and his penknife. They went out, and the key turned in the door.

Sometime during the afternoon the door opened again. A German soldier signaled John to follow him. He was taken out of the building, across a courtyard, into a second building, and down a hallway. They stopped at a door marked Kommandant. The soldier rapped smartly.

Someone inside answered. The soldier opened the door and gave John a little push to enter.

Sitting at a table was a Wehrmacht officer who, John guessed, was about forty years of age. On his uniform were the insignia of a major. He looked up at John and motioned for him to step forward.

On the table in front of the major was a topographical map. With a shock John saw that it was his own from the wrecked plane. He could see the red lines he had made marking the plane's course.

Quickly he tore his eyes away, hoping that his expression had not given him away.

The officer looked at him, not unkindly. "Your name?" he asked in perfect English.

John told him.

"Your number?"

"1378905, sir."

"Your rank?"

"Sergeant, sir."

"Your squadron number?"

John looked him in the eye. "I am a prisoner of war. By international law I am obliged to tell only my name, number, and rank. Please excuse me. I cannot answer any other questions."

The officer looked at the map on the table. "We know where you have come from. Why don't you admit it?"

"Please excuse me, sir."

"Look, we know you came from this aircraft that was shot down two nights ago. You were very lucky to survive."

John tensed inwardly for what was coming next, and gazed woodenly at the officer.

"The other six are dead."

John stared ahead, hoping that the confirmation of what he had feared did not show on his face.

The major went on questioning him. As he did so,

John began to realize that the officer was not sure that he was the seventh crew member of the wrecked plane. And John was not going to volunteer the information to him. As long as they are unsure, they will be spending time and money and employing personnel looking for a missing airman, he thought. That is fine as far as I am concerned.

Seeing that he was not going to get the information he needed from John, the major finally sent him back to his cell.

The next morning two German soldiers opened the door of the cell, and with that John began a train journey which ended at a *Luftwaffe* interrogation center, somewhere near Frankfurt, Germany.

The cell in which he found himself was a room with concrete walls and floor and measuring about six by ten feet. There was a small window with frosted glass and thick iron bars. The furniture consisted of a small wooden table and stool, a wooden bunk with a thin mattress, and two woolen army blankets. A bucket was on the floor, and a small tin washbasin stood on the table. A large radiator was near the wall with the window. John was grateful that his captors had his comfort so much in mind, but he wondered at so large a radiator in so small a room.

He was in the cell for not more than five minutes when an English-speaking *Luftwaffe* officer came and asked for his clothes and all of his possessions. John was left wearing only his underwear and his socks. He still had the hacksaw.

Finally a *Luftwaffe* enlisted man returned his clothes. As soon as the key turned in the lock, he checked to see whether they had found the maps. He was sure they would be gone. Incredibly, they and the compass were still hidden in the waistband of his trousers.

For thirteen days John was in solitary confinement, his loneliness and boredom broken only when he was taken out to be questioned regarding his identity. One day a civilian came to visit him, introducing himself as a member of the International Red Cross. It was his job, he said, to see that the names of all British Air Force prisoners were properly reported to the English.

After a friendly conversation he asked John his name, number, and rank. John told him. Then he casually asked John's parents' name.

John looked at the man and smiled. "Look, you're no more an International Red Cross representative than I am. You're a fake. We were warned about tricks like this."

Flustered, the man tried to argue. Finally he left.

John found the boredom almost insufferable. After a time he asked for something to read. A sympathetic guard brought him an English Bible. He began to read the Gospels and to find comfort in them. Then he began to pray—selfish prayers they were, he knew—prayers for release from his wretched condition, for freedom so that he could go home. In spite of his motives for praying, he did feel that God was near him. During his confinement he began to experience a relationship with God. However, he soon forgot about it when circumstances got better.

The March nights were chilly in his cold cement cell, but there was never any heat in the radiator. He often wondered why it had been put in the room.

After he had been in the cell for four or five days and his captors had still not gotten the information they wanted, he awoke about midnight one night to find his blankets on the floor and he himself bathed in perspiration. The room was like an oven. The radiator was almost red hot.

Banging on the door, he tried to get the attention of the guard, but nobody came.

Realizing at last that he was not going to get any attention, he removed most of his clothes and lay down again. After a long time he managed to doze off.

Toward morning he awoke to find himself shivering. The room was back to its customary chilliness.

During the day one of his interrogators inquired solicitously whether he had slept well, and suggested that he would sleep better if he would volunteer the information they needed. John said nothing.

The next night the same thing happened, and the next, but John refused to capitulate, in spite of the way he was wearing down. His captors began to get impatient. One of them threatened to turn him over to the Gestapo.

The heat treatment continued night after night. John knew that he could not resist indefinitely, but it appeared that his jailers were prepared to continue the torture indefinitely. Stubbornly he held on.

After more than a week of trying to sleep in the oven he could hold out no longer. He agreed to tell them the number of his squadron. The information he gave confirmed to his jailers that he was indeed the missing member of the plane that had been shot down near Reims on March 10.

That same day John was taken from the cell and learned that he was in Dulagluft, a small prisoner-of-war camp where noncommissioned Royal Air Force prisoners were kept temporarily until they could be transferred to a larger camp.

The camp to which he was now taken was about three hundred feet square and surrounded by double barbed-wire fences about four feet apart and eight feet high. Rolls of tangled barbed wire were in the space between the fences and inside the fence in the compound. Next to the inside fence were light poles placed about every thirty feet. At each of the four corners of the camp small roofed sentry boxes—goon boxes, the prisoners called them—were built above the wire fence. In each box were two sentries armed with rifles. About fifteen feet from the fence and twelve inches from the ground a wire went all

John's POW camp was surrounded by barbed wire and goon boxes.

the way around the compound. It marked the boundary of the compound for the prisoners. Anyone touching it could be shot.

Four single-story wooden barracks stood in the middle of the compound. John was escorted by two guards to one of them.

Fifteen or twenty men were in the room to which John was taken. He noticed that they were all sergeants, like himself. Some were lying on bunks reading. Others were talking together. John felt a great sense of relief to be among his own group again.

All gathered around John and began to ask him questions.

One of the group especially caught John's attention. He was a tall, ungainly, bearlike fellow with a hooked nose and bulging eyes. A high, narrow forehead appeared even higher because he was bald on top. His black hair grew thick at the sides. John guessed his age to be about thirty.

When the other fellows finally drifted back to their previous occupations this one approached John and introduced himself. His name was Jack Mason, a Londoner. He was a pilot who had been shot down.

After they had talked awhile, Mason looked around furtively, dropped his voice, and asked, "Do you want to get out of here?"

"Sure! I've already tried to escape."

Mason took him by the arm. "Let's go for a walk."

As they made a circuit around the camp Mason explained his scheme. He had been in the camp for nine days. During that time he had become acquainted with the habits of some of the guards. He had noticed that one particular change of guards had the habit of switching on the perimeter lights every three minutes. They would leave them on for precisely one-half minute, then off for three minutes. In this procedure they acted like clockwork, Mason had noticed. The other guards switched the lights off and on irregularly.

"These guards should come on at midnight tonight," Mason went on. "If we're going to escape we've got to do it tonight. It's our last chance. They're going to move us to a big camp before those guards come on again."

John looked dubiously at the formidable barbed-wire fences with the rolls of wire inside and between.

"Jack, how can we ever get over those fences in three minutes?"

"We won't go over them." He glanced around, then nodded surreptitiously at one of the guard boxes. Like the others on the compound, it was built on wooden stilts over a concrete pillbox. Between the top of each pillbox and the floor of the guard box was a space about eighteen inches high. A dirt road passed the camp just outside the fence near the guard box that Mason had indicated. Across the road was a fairly large stand of pine trees.

"We go over the fence right under a goon box!" John exclaimed incredulously.

"Sure. Then we won't have to worry about the barbed

wire between the fences. Not only that, but if we get caught under the goon box when the lights come on, the guards in the other boxes won't dare fire at us for fear of hitting their own men. And the goons in the box won't be able to hit us. Besides, they don't have machine guns, only rifles. That's a great advantage."

John pondered for a moment the difference between having one bullet and several in him.

"Why did you pick on me, anyway?"

"Frankly, I have tried all the others. None of them is willing to take a chance."

"I don't blame them. It sounds like a crazy idea to me too. What about the barbed wire on this side of the fence? You've still got to get over that."

"Don't you think I've figured out that too?" Mason responded a bit impatiently. "We'll take a door off one of the wardrobes in the barracks, tie a blanket around it, lay it across the barbed wire, and climb over it. I've got some food I've been saving."

For a moment John caught his enthusiasm. "I have my escape maps."

"Bully for you!"

Then John shook his head. "Jack, this idea is crazy!" He didn't say it but he thought to himself, And I think you're a bit crazy also.

But then a great desire to escape from the months, even years, in prisoner-of-war camps that might lie ahead surged through him. He might never again have such a chance to get away. He went over Mason's plan in his mind.

Then he said, "But what about the noise? That wire will make a great racket."

Mason made an impatient gesture. "I've thought of that one too. For several hours each night the wind comes up pretty strong. The noise from the wire and those trees across the road will drown out any noise we will make."

That fellow isn't such a fool after all, John thought.

He has figured out just about everything. Then he made a quick decision, "O.K., I'll join you."

They continued to walk slowly around the camp as they went over the plans again.

"But three minutes won't give us enough time to get out of the barracks and over the fence."

"We'll do this in two stages. There are no guards patrolling inside or outside the fence. If you'll look at the light poles you will see they are in such a position that the lights don't light up the area between our barracks and the next. The barracks' doors will be closed, but we can get through the window with the wardrobe door while the lights are off. We'll hide in the shadows until they turn the lights out the next time, then we'll get a move on."

"O.K. You've got everything planned, Jack. I'm with you."

"This is not going to be a walkover," Mason warned. "Nobody has ever gotten away from here before. We are taking a risk."

The afternoon dragged. John tried to get a little sleep, but he would doze off only to awaken with thoughts of the night's escapade running through his mind. Around five o'clock he and Mason ate some of the food rations they had received.

At seven-thirty several guards visited each of the barracks for the final inspection of the day. When they left, they closed the doors behind them.

After the guards had left the compound, John and Mason removed a door from one of the wardrobes and tied a blanket around it. Then they waited for the long hours to pass until midnight. They said little to the other men in the room, who had decided that Mason had finally found someone as crazy as himself.

With maddening slowness the hours dragged on. Doubts concerning the wisdom of the plan of escape nagged John's mind. But the thought of the way the others would ridicule him if he backed down now kept him from changing his mind.

After a time the lights in the barracks were switched off, the talking finally stopped, and then the sound of rhythmic breathing told John that only Mason and he were awake.

It was after eleven o'clock now, and all was quiet outside. The wind that Mason had predicted had not started. But in a few minutes the sound of gently rustling leaves whispered through the night. Gradually the sound became louder. By the time the luminous hands of John's watch approached the hour of midnight the rushing of the wind through the trees, the creaking of the branches, and the rattling of the wire fence convinced him that any noise they made would be amply muffled by it.

"It's midnight," Mason whispered.

Tensely they looked at their watches. Had Mason been correct in his calculations? Was he right concerning the guards who would come on duty? If he was, would they maintain their previous habit with the lights?

The lights came on. With tense interest they began to count the seconds. One. Two. Three. . . . Twenty-seven. Twenty-eight. Twenty-nine. Thirty.

Abruptly the lights went out.

Mason nudged John with an elbow. "It's them."

Now, would the guards wait exactly three minutes before they turned the lights on again?

John kept his eyes fastened on his watch. With maddening deliberateness the minute hand crept around the dial. One minute. Two minutes. Two and a half minutes. The hand moved on toward twelve. Three minutes!

Suddenly the compound was flooded with light.

"What did I tell you?" Mason whispered exultantly. "It's them. Bless their Teutonic methodicalness! Come on, let's not wait!"

John's heart was thumping wildly. They carried the blanketed door to the window. As soon as the lights went out Mason climbed through. John passed the door to him and followed. Heavy clouds raced across the sky, blanketing out the stars. They crept forward in the shadows as far as they safely could, ready to run as soon as the lights went off the next time. They had agreed that Mason would go first, carrying the food. If John didn't get away, Mason would not be stuck with nothing to eat.

The lights came on. His nerves on edge, John waited for them to go off. Then they grabbed the door and dashed for the corner guard box. John was infinitely grateful for the clouds that intensified the darkness and for the noise the trees and wires made.

Arriving below the guard box they swiftly placed the door across the roll of wire. Immediately and with awful dismay they learned that the door was not long enough to span the wire. Because of the curve at the corner it expanded out so that it was wider than at other places.

Time was of the essence. What were they to do?

"You go. I'll hold it!" Mason whispered urgently.

There was no time to argue. Quickly John climbed across the teetering door while Mason tried to steady it. When he got below the guard box the door teetered down. Grabbing for a post under the box he clawed himself to the top of the pillbox. Above him as he lay on his stomach breathing hard he could hear one of the guards move his feet. So far less than a minute had passed.

He could hear Mason trying to get across the door. But with no one holding it, it was making a great deal of noise.

Is it possible the guards aren't going to hear that? John wondered.

Suddenly there was a shout from above John's head, and the lights came on. Craning his head around, he saw Mason jump backwards from the wire into the compound, his hands as high in the air as he could reach.

John hardly dared to breathe, but he had to do something quickly.

The light that flooded the compound also lighted up

the road running along outside. Hoping that the attention of all the guards would be focused on Mason, he quickly wriggled across the pillbox, slid over the side, dropped the eight feet to the ground, and landing on his feet ran down the brilliantly lighted road away from the camp.

By now the guards were lustily blowing their whistles signaling an attempted escape.

Expecting at any instant to hear the sharp crack of a rifle, John raced down the road in an irregular zigzag pattern. But no shot came. On and on he fled until he was well away from the camp, and the darkness swallowed him.

He slowed to a dogtrot until the tall shadows of trees loomed ahead. With a tremendous sense of relief he plunged into them. Panting, he sank down with his back against a tree trunk with an exhilarating sense of freedom. He was at liberty. Even if he was caught in a short time, it would be worth it, he felt.

Then his spirits dropped abruptly. He suddenly realized that he didn't have any food. It was all with Mason.

The Road to Switzerland

AFTER JOHN HAD gotten his breath and rested for a few moments he decided he had better get as far from the prison camp as possible. Perhaps his disappearance had already been discovered. A search party might even now be starting out to look for him.

A star-studded sky interspersed with a few clouds showed through the tops of the trees. The wind was still blowing briskly.

Taking his bearing by the stars, John made his way through the forest in a general southwesterly direction. After about a half hour the trees thinned out and he found himself crossing meadowland with here and there a small stand of trees.

When daylight came he found a secluded spot in the middle of one of the stands of trees, and, stretching out under a tree, was soon asleep.

In about three hours he awoke with hunger gnawing at his stomach. But there was nothing to do but try to ignore it.

During the day between naps he thoroughly memorized from his maps the section of the country through which he was passing. By continuing on his present route he would come to a road leading to Mainz. He decided to try to cross the Rhine at that city, go south toward France, then try to cross the border into Switzerland. There he could contact the British consulate. They would have ways of getting him back to England.

As soon as dusk began to fall, with hunger as his ever more insistent companion, John left his copse and started off across the meadows.

Several hours passed, and he crossed several little country roads before coming to a paved road that he knew must be the one leading to Mainz.

Occasionally he passed a farmhouse back from the road, but each was in darkness. His eyes and ears were sharpened for any signs of life, but he detected none.

About one o'clock in the morning the low murmur of a river reached his ears, and he knew he was nearing the Rhine and, he hoped, the city of Mainz. The sound gradually grew louder, then he distinguished through the darkness the outline of a bridge.

Keeping close to the side of the road and taking advantage of all the cover he could John stealthily approached the bridge.

He stopped, his heart thumping. What was that sound? Hardly daring to breathe he remained utterly still, hoping he was hidden in shadows.

Minutes passed before he dared stir. Then taking advantage of all possible cover he moved closer to the bridge. Would there be guards? Certainly any bridge this important in England would be guarded, he thought.

Finally he was convinced that there were no guards on his side of the bridge, at least. As noiselessly as possible he started across, trying to melt into the stonework.

With pounding heart he approached the other end, straining his ears and eyes for any sign of guards. Again he could detect none. All was silent except for the purling of the river below.

Now he was on the other side. Is it possible that I can simply walk through an enemy city in the dead of night? he wondered.

The dark silhouette of buildings loomed ahead. But he had hardly turned down the street than his way was barred by great heaps of rubble. By the faint light of the stars he could see on each side of the street jagged masonry where large buildings had been. Bomber command had recently been at work on the city!

Another road turned to the left and followed along the river. Taking this, John walked until he found a street going south. Concealing himself as much as possible in the shadows of the dark buildings, he hurried along, hoping that a patrolling policeman would not suddenly round a corner and confront him. Here and there he saw further signs of bomb damage. Occasionally he had to climb over heaps of rubble. In about half an hour he was across town and heading southwest down a paved road through open country.

Slowly the miles dropped behind and the night passed. When the sky began to lighten John looked around for some place to hide. He was still passing through open farmland, which did not afford many places of concealment.

A pile of hay about three feet high in a field to his left drew him. Burrowing inside, he arranged the hay so that he could not be seen, and dozed off. But every few minutes hunger would awaken him.

He was beginning to feel weak now. He knew that unless he could find some food he would have to give himself up before many more hours passed.

By midmorning his hunger would not be denied. Pushing aside the hay, he looked around carefully. The fields were empty; the road stretched solitary in both directions.

Crawling out he stood up, brushed the hay from his clothes, and looked around. In the field across the road a few hundred yards south he saw some long, low mounds of earth. He recognized them as the type of mounds under which farmers preserved potatoes. With the remembered taste of juicy raw potatoes in his mouth, John hurried to the mound and began to dig away the dirt with his hands. A few inches under the soil his probing fingers found a layer of straw and then a vegetable of some sort. Pulling it out and rubbing off the dirt, he found to his disgust and disappointment that it was a mangel, a type of beet used to feed cattle.

Rubbing more of the dirt off, he tore off the outside of the mangel with his teeth, then bit into the white flesh. Raw mangel, he discovered, is not a palatable diet for people, even though cattle seem to relish it. To add to his misery the vegetable made him very thirsty. There was no sign of water anywhere around.

After eating all of the mangel he could stomach, John returned to the hay and again tried to sleep. But sleep would not come. The mangel had stilled the worst of the hunger pangs, but the thirst was worse than the hunger.

As the afternoon wore on his wretchedness was aggravated by the hay that found its way down his neck, up his trouser legs, and into his ears.

Finally he could stand it no longer. Desperately he decided to take a chance and keep on going.

The road continued south through gently rolling farmland. He passed a few farmhouses back from the road, but caught no glimpse of anybody.

After walking six or seven miles he began to approach a hamlet of half a dozen houses. Hesitatingly he kept on. To continue meant taking a chance, but to turn back might arouse the suspicion of anyone chancing to see him.

Making up his mind, he kept on walking.

But suppose someone saw him and decided to pass the time of day? His freedom would soon end.

An idea struck him. Pulling his handkerchief from

his pocket, he held it to his face as though he had a toothache and strode purposefully on.

As he neared the houses a middle-aged man in farm clothes came around the side of a barn on the left side of the road and caught sight of him. John's pulse quickened.

The man called out. John wasn't sure whether it was a greeting or a question. Without slowing he waved his free hand and gave a whimsically pained groan. The farmer waved back and turned away with a laugh.

Not daring to look back John kept on briskly down the road, expecting at any moment to hear the man shout after him or to see someone come from one of the houses.

About a half mile down the road he decided he had taken too much of a chance. He could have easily been caught. He had better get back into hiding.

Ahead, the road went up a small hill. When he came to the brow of the hill he saw about a quarter of a mile down the road a group of buildings that he recognized as a small railway station. He must be nearing another village or a small town. It would be wise to get out of sight immediately.

The small rise on which he stood was covered with low bushes. Quickly he crawled into them and found a place where he could observe what was going on ahead without being seen himself.

The railroad station was composed of four or five small buildings—a freight shed, a ticket office, and two or three smaller sheds with a few people working around them. A single-track railway line ran past the little platform.

Leaning against the freight shed was a bicycle.

A plan began to take shape in John's mind. The border of Vichy, France, was, he estimated, about sixty miles away. He had to get there if he was going to get help and get to Switzerland. Perhaps in France he would be able to contact a resistance organization that would arrange to get him to Switzerland or even England. That bicycle would help him get into France far quicker than he could by foot. If the bicycle was still there by nightfall, he would "borrow" it.

When a few hours later in the darkness John silently approached the railway station, only a glimmer of light in the ticket office told him that anyone was around. Tense, ready to freeze at the least sound or movement, he slipped up to the shed. The bicycle was still there. Hugging the wall, he slid along the platform. Gripping the bicycle by the frame, he lifted it and carried it to the road. In his weakened condition it seemed to weigh a hundred pounds, but he did not dare to wheel it for fear it would make a noise.

Unsteadily he mounted and cycled southward as fast as he could, passing through the village without seeing anyone.

By midnight he estimated he had traveled twenty-five or thirty miles. Weakness forced him to stop for rest from time to time, still he thought he would have no trouble getting to the French frontier before morning.

The road was uphill now. At the top was a village. He had intended to stay on the road and go right through the village, but a kind of presentiment caused him to look for a way around.

A dirt road ran off to the left. He decided to take it. In about a hundred yards it began to swing to the right. Then abruptly it dipped at a steep angle, and John found himself careening down an unknown road on a bicycle that was out of control. He was going so fast that the brakes could not hold him. Desperately he hung on, squeezing the brake levers without effect.

In the semidarkness he could see that the road turned sharply to the right at the foot of the hill—much too sharply for him to make it at the speed he was going.

The next moment he was hurtling through the air. Crashing through vegetation of some kind, he landed on his back with a jarring thud.

For a few moments he lay dazed. Then shakily he got to his feet. He seemed to be all right.

His fall, he discovered, had been broken by some grapevines hung from trellises. He was in a vineyard.

Making his way through the vines he found the bicycle lying in the road. It had smashed into a small embankment and thrown him off. To his dismay he found that the front wheel was hopelessly buckled.

Picking it up, he carried it well into the vineyard so that it would not be discovered too soon. He was back to walking.

John felt desperate. He was getting into his third day without any real food. Hunger now drove him to take chances. Each time he came to a house he stealthily investigated doors and windows hoping to get inside and find food. All were securely locked.

Exploring one house about four o'clock in the morning he found the door of the basement unlocked. His heart pounding with excitement, he went inside and closed the door. Feeling around in the darkness, he found a switch and turned on the light. He was in a storage room with shelves lining one side. Expectantly he looked for jars or tins of food, but the shelves were empty.

Then he saw a large tin in a far corner of one of the shelves. Excitedly he picked it up and shook it. It was full of something. The label in German told him nothing.

Going to the door he switched off the light, stepped outside, and hurried off. Now he had some food—but how was he going to get the tin open? His hacksaw was in his pocket, where he had put it after taking it out of his sock the first day of his escape, but he didn't think of it.

Dawn was slowly lighting the sky. Stopping beside the road a half mile from the house, John found a stone and began to pound on the cover of the tin. With watering mouth he finally managed to make a hole big enough to get at the contents. To his disappointment he found they were pickled gherkins.

Although they were not satisfying they were at least filling, and he felt better after he had eaten a number of them. With the tin in his hand, he kept on walking down the road.

His problem now was to find some place to hide for the day. Desperately he looked around, but there was only flat treeless farmland. Anxiously he kept on down the road, feeling very conscious of his unkempt appearance. If he could clean himself up a little, perhaps he would not look quite so conspicuous.

A shallow ditch at the base of two lone trees beside the road attracted him. The concealment offered there was only illusionary, but he decided to try to tidy up.

He was industriously brushing himself off when a sound caused him to look up. Approaching from the same direction he had come was a young woman dressed for farm work riding on a bicycle. Their eyes met, and apprehensively John felt her scrutinizing gaze. He was sure it was not altogether his imagination that told him she began to pedal faster when she passed him.

With a trapped feeling he looked around for a hiding place, but there was no place to hide.

To the left about two miles away was a village on a rise of land. Ahead of him about the same distance away was a forest. If only he could get there before being caught, perhaps he would be safe. He began to hurry.

The staccato of a motorcycle engine caught his ear. Looking down the road John realized that the game was up. A man—a policeman—was riding toward him.

Throttling down when he reached John, the burly middle-aged man got off, kicked down the stand for his cycle, put his hand on his revolver at his side, and said something in German.

John lifted his hands halfway up, still holding the can of gherkins. "English. *Kriegs Gefangener* ["prisoner of war"]."

"*Ausweis* ["identification"]?"

From an inside pocket of his jacket John produced his prisoner-of-war identity tag and showed it to the policeman.

Remounting his cycle, the policeman indicated that John was to continue walking while he idled along just behind him.

Now John began to think of the implications of the tin of gherkins in his hand. It was not a crime to be an escaped prisoner of war. But breaking into a home and stealing was. The policeman did not seem to be paying any attention to the tin, but somehow John felt he had to get rid of it.

After walking about a mile he gave his captor to understand that he needed to rest.

The policeman was sympathetic and signaled for him to sit at the roadside. When John got up, he simply walked away from the gherkins. To his relief the policeman gave no sign that he had noticed.

In about an hour they arrived at a small town, and John was escorted to the jail and put in a cell. As the policeman was about to lock the door John said, "*Essen* ["Food"]."

The man smiled and nodded. John threw himself down on the wooden bunk and waited impatiently.

In about ten minutes the policeman returned with a tin tray on which were the usual sausage, thick piece of rye bread, and cup of ersatz coffee. With shaking hands John wolfed it down. When he had finished he lay back on the bunk. He felt much better, but he could have eaten more. In a few moments he fell into a sound sleep.

Tunneling for Freedom

THE SOUND OF a key turning in the
lock of the cell door awakened John. The
policeman entered carrying a tray on which
were a bowl of soup and some more bread.
It was the noon meal.

After he had eaten, John felt refreshed
and ready to think of escape again.

The small barred window overlooked
a narrow alley. Examining the iron bars,
he decided he would need to cut two
to get out. The policeman had given
him to understand that some soldiers
were coming to take him back to the
POW camp. John hoped they wouldn't
come until the next day. Given a night
in the cell he thought he could cut through
the bars and get away before morning.
He began sawing right away.

The bars were of good quality iron
and made for hard cutting. He was about
halfway through the first bar when he
heard the key rattling in the door. Whip-
ping the hacksaw into his pocket, he
quickly sat on the bunk.

The door opened, and John's heart
sank. Standing in the doorway behind
the policeman were two young soldiers

dressed in the field-gray uniforms of the German army.

As John looked at them he sensed that he had better be careful. Up to this point he had been treated more or less courteously, even sympathetically, by his captors. But a look of cold arrogance on the faces of these men warned him.

Curtly one of them ordered him to his feet and frisked him none too gently. He didn't detect the hacksaw. Then with a shove John was escorted through the door. At a brisk pace the three of them marched down the village street to a small station as villagers looked on curiously.

A few minutes later a passenger train chugged in, and John was hustled aboard one of the carriages. The soldiers commandeered a compartment occupied by three or four civilians. John was directed to sit on one side of the compartment; the soldiers sat facing him on the other.

In about an hour the train rolled into a station that a sign proclaimed to be Neustadt. Brusquely John was ordered out and taken to a waiting army truck. He was directed to climb into the covered rear of the vehicle. His guards climbed in after him.

After a drive of about ten minutes the truck came to a stop, there was an exchange of conversation, then the sound of an opening gate. As they drove through, John saw barbed-wire fence and guards. He was inside a prisoner-of-war camp once more. It proved to be a camp for French prisoners.

After a brief interpreted interrogation by the camp commandant, John was placed in a solitary-confinement cell.

The next morning two *Luftwaffe* guards came for him in a car and informed him he was being returned to Dulagluft.

It was late afternoon when they arrived at the camp. John was taken to the same interrogation block where he had spent thirteen days before his escape, and locked in a solitary-confinement cell.

As he sat glumly on the edge of his bunk he wondered whether he would be kept in solitary confinement for some time for his escape or given some other even more stringent punishment.

In about a half hour a guard unlocked the door and announced, "Commandant."

John jumped to his feet as the officer entered and gave him a salute. The commandant looked at John for a moment, then sat on the bunk. Smiling, he motioned for John to sit down also.

"Curnow, I came to congratulate you," he said in perfect English. "You are the first prisoner to escape over the fence." He paused. "And I am making sure you will be the last."

John grinned. "What's going to happen to me now?"

"You'll be going back into camp. I just wanted to meet you."

After a few more moments of conversation the officer stood up. John came to attention and saluted. The commandant acknowledged his salute, and left.

The next morning John was taken to the prisoner-of-war compound, much to his relief. As he was escorted through the gate he saw the reason for the commandant's remark that there would be no more escapes from the camp. Deadly looking machine guns had replaced the rifles at each guard box.

John learned that a group of prisoners had been moved from Dulagluft during his absence. Mason was among them.

Five days after John had been returned to the camp another group of prisoners was transferred to a permanent prisoner-of-war camp. He was one of them. Under heavy guard they were marched to the nearby railway station and taken to Stalag-Luft III at a place called Sagan, some eighty miles south of Berlin.

Stalag-Luft III was a three-sectioned camp set in a clearing of a pine forest. The first section was the camp for R.A.F. officer prisoners. The center section was used for senior noncommissioned officers. John and the men with him were taken to this compound. The third section was the *Forelager,* the administrative area containing the office of the commandant and barracks for the guards and supply buildings.

Two eight-foot-high barbed-wire fences surrounded the enclosure with the eight feet of space between them filled with rolls of barbed wire. At intervals along the fence were goon boxes, small sentry boxes set on stilts above the fence. They were armed with machine guns and searchlights that swept the camp continually during the night. At intervals between the goon boxes were arc lights set on poles above the fence.

A single strand of wire called a warning wire placed twelve inches above the ground ran around the entire circumference of the camp fifteen feet inside the fence. Any prisoner even touching this trip wire was liable to be shot by the guards. Just inside the wire was a path worn by the prisoners as they walked around the camp.

The barracks—big single-story wooden buildings raised on piles about eighteen inches above the ground—were in the center of the compound.

The elevation of the barracks was to permit the sentries and ferrets to see under them, thus hindering the digging of escape tunnels.

The ferrets were Germans whose job it was to discover and head off any efforts of the prisoners to escape, which efforts were constantly being made by some. Dressed in overall-type suits and three-quarter boots, these men were constantly poking around inside the barracks, concealing themselves under the huts, or endeavoring to sneak up on a group of prisoners on the chance that they might discover something. It hardly needs saying that these men were extremely unpopular with the prisoners. At the same time there was an element of mutual respect between them, and they were con-

Inside the wire the POW's wore a path as they walked around the camp.

stantly trying to outwit one another, sometimes with a certain amount of humor.

Each of the long barracks was separated into two similarly arranged sections with a door in the dividing partition so that one could go through the whole building. At the far end of each of the rooms were two smaller rooms that were used for kitchens. The men did their own cooking in these rooms.

The wooden bunks were built in sets of eight—four below and four above. Board partitions separated the bunks so that the kriegies, the term the men used to describe themselves as prisoners of war, had a certain amount of privacy. There were about ten such bunk units in John's room, belonging to eighty kriegies. John's was a lower bunk near a window.

As John looked around him when he first entered his barracks he saw what seemed like a strange lot of men. Some of them, he learned later, had been there for two and one-half years as prisoners. Some were bearded, with whiskers that ranged in color from black to fiery red. They were dressed in a great variety of clothes, the light blue of the Royal Air Force, and the dark blue of the Australian Air Force, and many were dressed in khaki British uniforms received through the Red Cross for British prisoners of war. Later when the chill of autumn came on balaklava helmets, sweaters, scarfs, and great-coats of every description would be worn. For footwear they shuffled around in everything from flying boots to wooden clogs. In warm weather many went around with bare feet.

On rough shelves fastened to the boards around each bed were the few private possessions of each POW—a photograph or two, a few dog-eared books, Red Cross food boxes, old tins. Each was treasured for the memories or the utility it offered.

As was the case whenever a new man arrived in camp, the others in the barracks gathered around John to learn his story and any news from the outside world he might have. One of the men, noting his youthfulness, remarked, "What's the R.A.F. doing now, anyway? Robbing the cradle?"

The first night John was in the barracks he learned that the camp radio was there. Radios were, of course, illegal in the camp. But one had been smuggled in tube by tube and wire by wire by some German guards who had been bribed with cigarettes, coffee, and chocolate received in Red Cross parcels.

It was concealed, John discovered, at the back of the first-aid box in the kitchen. To all appearances, the box was screwed securely to the wall. But it had a concealed hinge so that it swung away, revealing the small radio fastened to its back. There was just enough space between the inner and outer wall to put the tubes.

Across the kitchen several wires were strung, ostensibly for hanging dishcloths on. The large barracks room also had wire strung entirely around it, which was used by the men to hang their washing on. The whole system of wires was joined and utilized as an aerial.

John was told that he was to keep away from the kitchen at six in the evening. At that time if no ferret was around the men in charge of the radio listened to the B.B.C. news. The whole thing was done systematically. There were four men on the team: the operator, who would stand before the radio listening by earphones, a man standing behind him to snatch off and conceal the earphones in case a ferret came by, another to snatch away the wire connecting the radio to the aerial, and a fourth to slam shut the cabinet. The whole thing could be done in three seconds. While the radio was in use there was always a group in the kitchen cooking their evening meal so that everything would appear normal should a ferret happen by.

Soon after John arrived at the camp he began to inquire about Mason. He learned that he had been sentenced to two weeks of solitary confinement for trying to escape. John expected to be sent to the cooler for escaping. He never was. He learned that the commandant who interviewed him had not sent a report of his escape to this camp.

When Mason got out of solitary confinement John

looked him up. Mason listened with keen interest to John's account of his escape. Then they began to discuss the possibilities of escape from Stalag-Luft III.

"Let's go for a walk and look things over," Mason suggested.

As they walked around the camp and looked at the heavy fences, the machine guns, the guards patroling the camp, both inside and out, escape began to look hopeless.

"The only way of getting out of here seems to be by tunnel," Mason said. "But everything has been looked over pretty carefully. There doesn't seem to be much more that can be done."

At the end of the camp near the fence separating them from the administration area was one of the washrooms and a toilet block, set off from the prisoners' barracks. As they approached this brick building they began to eye it speculatively.

Inside the washroom, running the width of the room against either wall, were two long wash benches. Two shorter ones were fastened to each other in the center. Water pipes ran the length of each bench with taps every three or four feet. The benches sloped inward so that the waste water ran into drains that emptied through a pipe in the center of each bench. These pipes led into concrete lined pits in the floor at the center of each bench. Pipes leading away from them conveyed the water to a soakaway area between the building and the fence.

"The only possible place in here to dig a tunnel would be from there," John observed, pointing to one of the square concrete pit openings.

"It wouldn't work," Mason objected. "They have been thought of before. They are too small for a person to squeeze through."

Leaving the washhouse they continued their walk around the compound in pensive silence.

After a time Mason said, "John, let's go back and measure one of those pits."

Casually they sauntered back to the washhouse. Diagonally, the pits measured twenty inches, just big enough for a man to squeeze through.

"Say, we can make a tunnel from here!" Mason exclaimed. "Let's go outside and see in which direction it should go."

Outside, John nodded cautiously toward an area in the German administrative area. "There's the place to take our tunnel."

On the other side of the barbed wire separating the two compounds, about thirty feet inside the fence, was a small woodshed. It was some distance from the other buildings, diagonally from where they stood. A better place for surfacing a tunnel could hardly be imagined. Moreover, the fences around the administrative area were not guarded. Once the woodshed was reached, it would be a comparatively simple job to get away. They estimated that the tunnel would have to be 120 feet long.

They would, of course, need help to make the tunnel. So the thing to do was to take their idea to the escape committee appointed by the prisoners. They approached the chairman and explained their idea. After looking the situation over the committee decided the tunnel was feasible. Work was begun on it immediately. John and Mason were not included on the digging team. That was left to more experienced men. It was early May, 1943.

It was essential that no clue be given to the ferrets or guards that anything unusual was going on in the washhouse. While the tunnel was being excavated via the pit, it was imperative that the impression be given that the wash bench was being used and that waste water was draining down the pit. Consequently, it was constantly splashed with water.

A false bottom made to fit the bottom of the pit was kept ready. After the digger was finished for the time being or warning was given that a ferret was approaching, the bottom was set in and the cover replaced.

POW's shored up escape tunnels with bed boards and scraps of wood.

The POW's were constantly on the watch for ferrets. A system of signals warned the diggers as soon as one was in the vicinity. John and Mason were appointed to the team of watchers.

To begin with, the pit was dug down about fifteen feet before leveling off. When that depth had been reached, a six-by-seven-foot chamber some seven feet high was made. It was necessary for the diggers to work properly.

Then the difficult work of tunneling the 120 feet began. A number of obstacles had to be overcome. There was the problem of getting fresh air into the narrow tunnel as it extended farther and farther. This was solved by contriving a pump from an old canvas kit bag. This, fastened to a pipe made of dried-milk tins, provided reasonably satisfactory circulation for the digger. Extra tins were added as the tunnel lengthened.

Someone came up with some electric wire, a socket, and a bulb. This was surreptitiously connected with the wiring of the washroom so that the digger had light. The excavated soil was taken from the tunnel by means of an eighteen-inch metal washpan. Holes were made across from each other in the rim of the basin. Ropes plaited from string off Red Cross parcels were tied in the holes. One piece of the rope was held by the digger, the other by a man in the chamber. The digger would drag the basin to where he was working and fill it. Then he would give a tug. The man in the chamber would drag it back, empty it, and signal the digger to pull it back again.

Another man stood at the top of the pit in the washroom pulling the soil up. This was carried out by men who "drifted" in with tall water jugs used to carry water to the barracks. When they left, the guards thought the jugs contained water. The soil was carefully distributed around the camp.

The big chamber was not quite finished when word came that the officer prisoners' camp was becoming crowded, and that theirs was being taken over for them. The 3,000 men in their camp were to be moved. This would be done at the rate of about 500 men at a time over the next three or four weeks. They would be moved by a train that would shuttle between the present camp and the next one every four or five days.

That none of the men working on the tunnel would lose his chance of escape, the escape committee arranged for the group to move to barracks that would be emptied last.

Also, because of the necessity now of getting the tunnel through as soon as possible, it was decided that instead of taking the longer, safer route to the woodshed, the tunnel would take the direct route under the fence into the administrative compound.

This posed another problem. The new direction led through the soil soaked by the waste water, which presented a danger that the tunnel would collapse. But it was decided that if the tunnel was to be finished before they were moved out, the chance would have to be taken.

The tunnel had progressed some 25 feet from the washhouse when it caved in. The sand poured into the tunnel, filling much of it, and a two-foot-wide hole appeared on the surface. Fortunately, no one was working in it at the time. The Germans cordoned off the washhouse and searched it thoroughly but did not discover the tunnel's outlet. They probed the ground with a long metal rod where the hole had appeared. Again, they did not discover the tunnel. They finally decided it was just a collapse of the soil caused by the seeping water, so they merely filled in the hole that had appeared on the surface.

The diggers waited a couple of days before digging again to be sure the guards had no suspicions. Two days were required to clean out the sand before progress could be made. But they had hardly started before the sand began to pour in again. The digger barely managed to get back to the large chamber and follow the others up the pit before the boards shoring up the tunnel collapsed. Another hole appeared on the surface.

This time the Germans were sure a tunnel was being dug. Again they carefully searched the washhouse, but could find nothing. Finally they dug down around the hole and discovered the half-filled tunnel. Determined to find out where it came from, they cleared it out, and then sent a man down to crawl along it to discover the entrance. While he was laboriously crawling along the tunnel, the German officers stood in the washhouse wondering where he would emerge. They were greatly surprised to see him crawl up through the drain pit.

A Leap From a Moving Train

A FEW DAYS later the Germans began to move the men in the camp by train. John's barracks was slated to be in the last trainload.

When the tunnel project failed, John began to plan for escape from the train. From the Red Cross packages that were received from time to time he had been hoarding powdered milk, cocoa, chocolate, and rolled oats. These he mixed together and baked into a flat cake that would be his escape rations. He also altered his uniform as much as he could to make it look civilian.

Gradually the camp emptied, and finally the morning came for the last group to leave. They were ordered to line up in rows five men wide to be marched the one and a half miles to the Sagan railway station.

As the prisoners fell in, the German guards were boasting that they had moved 2,500 men and not one of them had escaped. This made John all the more determined that there would be one.

As they marched away from the camp John looked longingly at the deep forest.

But there was no possibility of escape there. Any man breaking ranks would be shot.

The train itself was made up of a number of third-class cars with doors at each end. Guards were stationed at the doors. An aisle down the center of the car was flanked on each side by seats higher than the head accommodating three people. Iron luggage racks were fastened on the back of the seats above the head. John chose a seat near the center of the carriage to be as far as possible from the guards.

He noticed that the windows in the carriage were made to drop down inside the carriage wall. A leather strap fastened to the bottom of the window was used to raise and lower it. However, a bolt had been placed in the wood under each window so that it could not be moved. Additionally, each window was kept shut by four wooden wedges, driven two on each side between the sash and the window. Several heavy screws had been driven through the window and sash frames. Also a heavy bolt had been placed at the top of the window and another into the wall above it. These were wired together.

When John took his seat he was elated to discover that the bolt holding up his window was missing. Obviously the kriegie who had ridden in the seat on the last trip had been at work.

In a half hour the train began to move, and John was able to examine the other fastenings on the window. He soon began to realize that he had made a fortunate choice of seat. The four wedges had been worked loose, so that it would not take much more effort to get them out. The wire joining the two bolts had been loosened and sat on them lightly, and two of the screws were missing. The last prisoners occupying the seats had planned to escape, but either had not had the opportunity or the time. In any case, about all John had to do was remove the wedges, get the remaining screws from the window, and the window could be lowered. It seemed that the guards had become overconfident and had not carried out a security check on the train.

Word had gotten out among the prisoners that they were headed for a place in East Prussia. John's knowledge of the route told him that to get there the train would be cutting across a corner of Poland some time during the night or early morning. He decided to try to escape in Poland. He had a better chance of getting help there than in Germany.

It would be better if he had a companion or two in his escape, so he invited his two seatmates to join. Both demurred. Finally one of the men across the aisle agreed to join him. This man switched seats with the one sitting near John.

After working some time with the screws in the window, John finally had them loose enough so that he could quickly pull them out. All he and his companion had to do now was wait for the train to slow down sufficiently during the night for them to drop the window and jump through.

But the train did not slow down except twice, when it drew into stations to take on fuel and water. On those occasions the guards were especially on the alert, while others patroled outside.

Sleep weighed upon John, but he fought it off for fear he would miss his opportunity.

Slowly the night passed while he got more and more frustrated. Slowly the sky lightened. Daylight would make the chances of escape so hazardous as hardly to be feasible. In spite of this John had made up his mind that if the opportunity came he would jump anyway.

Gradually the light grew. Then John noticed that the train was slowing down. The heavy laboring of the engine ahead told him that they were going up a grade. The speed dropped off more and more.

"This might be our chance," he muttered to his companion.

Peering tensely out of the window, he saw that their chance had indeed arrived. They were slowly approaching a large field of corn some five feet high, which grew right down to the tracks.

"This is it!" he whispered to his companion.

"Not for me, Mack! Not in this light!"

There was no time for reasoning. Checking to see where the guards were, John quickly pulled out the wedges and the screws and let the window down by its strap. He had hung his knapsack around his neck. Now, trying to get through the window, he found that his sack stuck. Snatching it off, he tossed it out and jumped after it.

Hitting the ground, he rolled down a small embankment. Before he could pick himself up he heard warning shouts. Some guards had seen him.

His knapsack containing his food lay a few short yards away. But he knew that to go for it would be suicide. He would be shot down.

Doubling over, he ran as fast as he could through the corn, zigzagging as he went. As he ran he realized that again he had made a foolish mistake with the food. Not thinking he would not be able to get through the window with his sack, he had put all the food he had into it. He should have put some in his pockets.

He could hear the train grinding to a stop amid much shouting. But he figured that the guards would not try to find him. After all, there were 500 other kriegies back there that might take off in all directions if they were not watched. So he stopped running and crouched low in order that he would not be seen by any movement in the corn.

In about five minutes the train whistle blew, then John heard the train chug slowly up the hill and away. Once again the exhilarating sense of freedom surged over him that he had experienced after his first escape.

For a moment he considered going back for his

knapsack. But he ruled the idea out. There just might be a guard back there waiting for him.

He looked about him. He knew he was in Poland, but was not sure where. For the most part, open rolling country lay around him in the early morning sunshine, with only a few farmhouses scattered around.

All morning he walked in a northerly direction, avoiding houses and roads, and taking advantage of whatever cover offered itself. Toward noon he began to feel sleepy, so finding a stand of trees he concealed himself and was soon asleep.

Late in the afternoon he awoke refreshed, but decided to stay where he was until sundown.

In the dying glow of an amber twilight he crossed a field from the shelter of trees and arrived at a road. Silhouetted against the sky less than a quarter of a mile away and a little way back from the road was a small Polish cottage.

No hedge or fence separated the little cottage from the road. Slowly, concealing himself as much as possible, he approached the door and knocked quietly. It opened, and before him outlined by the light of a kerosene lamp was a middle-aged woman in a rough peasant's dress. John could sense apprehension in her attitude.

She said something in Polish, which he could not understand.

"English," said John, and made flying motions with his hands. "*Ich bin Englisch Flieger,*" he added in crude German.

Anxiously the woman looked outside to see whether anyone had seen them.

"*Menchen haben mich nicht gesehen* ["Nobody has seen me"]," he said.

She motioned him inside and quickly closed the door. John found himself standing in one of the two rooms of the little cottage. A rough wooden table stood under a small window with three chairs around it. The room, he noticed, was very clean. A girl twelve or thirteen years of age stood shyly in the shadows of one corner of the room.

"*Ich bin sehr hungrig* ["I am very hungry"]," he smiled.

The woman went to a little cupboard and brought him a large piece of rye bread with some margarine on a cracked porcelain plate. She poured a cup of ersatz coffee from a pot on a small stove. Motioning for him to sit at the table she placed the food before him, saying something in Polish. Then she said, "German," with a meaningful shrug. John understood she was trying to explain the reason for the meager fare.

While eating John asked in halting German whether she could help him get to Danzig, which he estimated to be about one hundred miles north, on the Baltic Sea. At this she showed extreme nervousness, and shook her head. John said no more except to indicate his thanks for the food.

When he had finished eating, she went outside to check whether anyone was around; then she signaled for him to come. He smiled at the young girl, who was still in the shadows, took the woman's hand and squeezed it gratefully, then slipped out into the darkness. The door closed quickly behind him.

Cautiously, keeping in the shadows until he was well away from the house, so as not to implicate the woman should he be caught, he continued on down the road. Bright starlight lighted the countryside, making travel easy.

John kept walking all night, guided by the North Star. Sometimes he followed the road, sometimes he cut across the fields.

Dawn came. The sun rose and began to climb the sky.

About eight o'clock he came to a narrow dirt road leading in the direction he wanted to go. He decided to follow it. When he had gone about half a mile down this road he saw in a yard ahead a small farmhouse and a few buildings. All of them were unpainted and unprosperous looking.

He paused a moment, undecided whether to stop. He could never be sure that the Polish farmer would risk helping him. But that was a chance he had to take. He went to the gate, opened it, and went into the yard.

Just as he turned away from the gate a man dressed in faded farm clothes emerged from the barn a few yards away with a medium-sized mongrel dog beside him. As soon as the dog saw John it began to bark furiously.

The farmer had a sharp, mean face. He spoke harshly in German. John understood what he was saying: "Who are you? What do you want? Where are you going?"

John groaned inwardly. Of all the luck! The farmer was not Polish but German. Probably he had moved onto this Polish farm after Germany had invaded Poland.

What should he do now? The man was of slight build. John was sure he could get away from him. But having to tangle with the dog was another matter.

Seeing John's hesitation, the farmer turned toward the house and shouted something. In seconds a woman ran out of the house with a pistol in her hand. The farmer took it from her and pointed it at John. John raised his hands shoulder high. The man signaled, higher. After giving his wife instructions, he indicated John was to go to the house. The woman hurried away to get help.

Inside the house John was directed to sit in a chair beside the table. The farmer sat across from him, rested his gun hand on the table, and pointed the pistol at John, with his finger on the trigger. John watched the trigger finger in nervous fascination. The man was jittery, and every time John moved even slightly the trigger finger reacted.

The minutes dragged on in silence as the farmer kept his eyes on John and John watched him and the deadly pistol barrel pointing straight at him.

About an hour had passed when John heard the farm-yard gate open, and then the sound of footsteps. In a few seconds a German soldier came through the door, a rifle slung over his shoulder. The farmer's wife entered behind him.

As soon as the soldier came through the door the farmer began to talk excitedly, still keeping the pistol pointed at John.

Interrupting, John spoke to the soldier and conveyed the idea that he would like him to tell the farmer to stop pointing the gun at him. Good-naturedly, he acquiesced and told the farmer to lay the pistol on the table.

John theatrically wiped his brow and gave a loud relieved sigh. The soldier laughed and said scornfully, "Civilian."

Although they were of necessity enemies, they were military men and felt a mutual disdain of dithery non-military.

Motioning to the door, the soldier said, *"Geht* ["go"]!" at the same time tapping the stock of his rifle significantly.

As he walked along in front of the soldier John did not feel low in spirits particularly, but he did feel humiliated that he had allowed himself to be caught so easily. He should have reconnoitered before calling at the farmhouse.

A short distance down the road he noticed a man in the battle dress of a British soldier working alone in a field nearby. A British army POW put to work on a farm by his captors, John realized. The man looked at John and asked, "Kriegie?"

"R.A.F.," John answered.

"Bad luck, mate."

John wished the soldier had been working in the field when he had passed there about an hour before. Things would have worked out differently.

The sun shone brightly, and John began to feel hot

and dusty as they marched along at a fast pace. In about an hour and a half they came to a small town. On its outskirts the soldier signaled John to turn down a tree-lined side road. In a few minutes they rounded a curve, and ahead, bulked against the sky, was an old gray fort built on a low rise.

Shortly they were at the tall barred gate. A guard swung it open, and their footsteps echoed against the gray stone walls as they marched into the cobbled courtyard inside.

A German officer sat behind a desk in the room to which John was escorted. In answer to his questions John displayed his prisoner-of-war identity disk and explained how he had escaped. After a few more questions he was taken to a barracks room, where he found a number of British soldiers. From them he discovered that the prison was near the Polish city of Thorn. The soldiers had been captured at Dunkirk three years before.

Two days later two *Luftwaffe* guards came for him. By train he was taken to a POW camp at Heydekrug, in South Lithuania, some ten miles east of the Baltic Sea. It was the end of June, 1943.

One of the first men to meet him was Jack Mason. "I've reserved a bunk for you in our barracks. I didn't think you'd get far."

Bleak Winters—and a Spring

THE CAMP AT Heydekrug was divided into two sections—one for Royal Air Force and the other for United States airmen. However, two high barbed-wire fences with rolls of barbed wire between and a warning wire on each side kept contact between the two groups at a minimum.

Some 3,000 men were in the R.A.F. camp. John was to spend most of the next 12 months there. During those months other prisoners were added, until by the time the year was up the camp's population had swollen to about 4,000 men.

The morale of the men was high. By means of a clandestine radio they were able to learn of the course of the war: that the Russians were advancing from the east, that the Allies had defeated the Germans in North Africa, and that Italy had been invaded.

The guards were aware that there was a radio in the camp. Many of the prisoners had maps on which they marked the latest positions of the battle fronts. These were not concealed, and the guards were able to study them. They knew

121

the information came from a radio, and they tried their best to find it. After a great deal of sleuthing they finally pinpointed the right barracks. Then one afternoon without warning they called a spot *Appel* ("parade").

As the prisoners fell in barracks by barracks in the parade area they realized by the large number of guards present that something was up. When all of the prisoners were in formation, the barracks in which the radio was secreted was cordoned off. Then two POW's were called out to witness the search of the building, according to International Law. This was to ensure that the guards could not be accused of theft or destructiveness.

The barracks was searched figuratively with a fine-toothed comb. But to the frustration of the searchers they did not uncover the radio. In the room was an old hand-crank phonograph set on a shelf. Through the Red Cross the prisoners had received a few records, which they played often. Baffled but still sure the radio was in the building the guards turned their attention to the old phonograph.

The witnessing prisoners, who understood German, heard one of them say, "The radio may be inside this."

"But how can we find out?"

"Let's break it open."

At this one of the POW's reminded them that, according to International Law, they would be personally responsible if they damaged the property of any prisoners, and would have to replace it.

Considering this, one of the guards said, "Let's see if it works. It couldn't if the radio was inside."

Putting on a record, they wound up the phonograph and started it playing. The sound of a Strauss waltz filled the room. Taking off the needle, they carefully replaced the phonograph on the shelf.

Imperceptibly the witnesses gave a sigh of relief. The radio was inside.

Food was a factor in keeping morale high. Red Cross

Red Cross parcels were welcomed with Canadian ones best liked.

parcels arrived regularly with food to supplement the camp diet of rye bread—usually from eight to twelve months old—vegetables, sauerkraut once or twice a month, meat occasionally, margarine every week or two, and an evil-smelling cheese ration the POW's called fish cheese. This they disdained to eat, although it would never do to refuse it. To do so would give the guards the excuse to say they were being fed too well, and thus make it possible to cut back on the rations. So they took it but surreptitiously buried it.

The Red Cross parcels were American, Argentinian, Australian, Canadian, and British. The Canadian parcels were the most popular. They contained such things as cans of dried milk, biscuits, cans of meat, butter, cheese, and chocolate. The high light of POW life in the camp was mail arrival. Everyone would crowd around the distributor. Even those who rarely, if ever, got letters from home would stand around hopefully, only to turn away disappointed when the last letter had been handed out.

In spite of the high morale, life in the camp was boring. John tried to study German and mathematics, taught by prisoners who had been teachers in civilian life, but he couldn't put his mind to it.

Autumn came. The nights grew longer. Cold winds began to blow from Finland across the Baltic Sea.

As the weeks passed and winter came, the cold became extreme. The men wore every scrap of clothes they possessed all the time. The only bedding provided was two coarse gray woolen blankets.

Earlier, John had managed to get some shredded paper, which came as packing around some of the Red Cross packages. Using it he made a sort of sleeping bag of his two blankets. The paper proved to have tremendous insulating qualities. His bed was situated close to a window, which was left open nights for ventilation. Many mornings he awoke to find the foot of his bed covered with snow, but he always slept warmly. Others were not so fortunate.

To escape the boredom John volunteered to work at ironing clothes in the laundry. This work brought him the advantage of being able to get a hot bath every week in half a wooden barrel used for a tub.

Slowly the long, bitterly cold, stormy winter wore away and spring, 1944, arrived. And with it came the Allied spring offensive. The prisoners learned that the Russians were advancing rapidly from the east.

Then in early June came the electrifying news that the continent had been invaded from the west—D Day.

Weeks went by, and the prisoners began to wonder whether the Russians would get to their camp before the Germans had a chance to evacuate them. Then the word came: Prepare to move out in three days. The only luggage they could take was what they could carry.

It was a strange and motley army of prisoners that marched, five abreast, flanked here and there by guards, from the Heydekrug POW camp. Most of them wore all the clothes they had. All started off overloaded. Some of the things were valuable—plates, mugs, cooking pots. Some were merely familiar things that seemed to offer a certain intangible security—gadgets made of old tins, nails, bits of string—things that under normal circumstances would have gone into the trash heap. These possessions were carried on crude wheelbarrows that in some cases broke after a quarter mile. Some men teamed up and made stretchers, which they piled with assorted belongings. Other men carried poles between them, from which their possessions were slung. John carried a knapsack, which he had stuffed with as many things as he could carry.

It proved to be a hot, dusty march—ten miles long. Soon the roadside was strewn with discarded items.

Finally the front of the more than half-mile-long column arrived at the railway station, their immediate destination. Word flashed back along the long column of what awaited them. The tidings brought gloom. They were to travel in enclosed cattle cars.

Each car was divided into three sections. The smaller, center section, which included the two doors, one on each side of the carriage, was for the guards. Barbed wire set off the other sections. Heavy wire doors fastened with stout locks secured these compartments.

Twenty men were crowded into each of the compartments. There was little room for one to lie down or to sleep. And there were no toilet or washing facilities.

Some fifteen or twenty minutes after John and nineteen other men were herded into a compartment the train started off with a jerk. John set his knapsack on the floor and squeezed down beside it. His feet pushed into another man, and someone's elbow was jamming into his back. Everybody shifted around to find a comfortable position, but comfort was not to be found.

They did not know where they were going. They knew only that they were heading into Germany.

The journey was made in two stages of three days each, with a three-week stopover between. This stopover was made at the prisoner-of-war camp at Thorn, in Poland, where John had been imprisoned briefly after his escape from the train.

John was immensely relieved that the journey was not made in one stage. As it was, each three-day trip made the prisoners feel like animals crowded in cages. The lack of toilet facilities, the cramped conditions, the multiplying vermin, made life a misery.

After a time, when the train came to one of its many stops, during the second three days, hardly anybody noticed. They were too benumbed. But after one other stop the guards began to shout some words that aroused them. They were at their destination.

A wave of relief, even a faint cheer, surged along the train. A prison camp, no matter how bad, could not possibly be as miserable as the cattle train.

The new camp, Falingbostel, was near Sulingen, some thirty miles south of Bremen.

Some time after their arrival at the camp food supplies began to dwindle. The problem occasioned by military setbacks forced their captors to give them less food than previously. But, worst of all, the Red Cross packages were no longer coming through. Allied raids on road and rail sometimes brought transportation almost to a standstill. Obviously, Red Cross parcels for prisoners of war would not be given priority under these circumstances. Previously, there had been one parcel for each man. Now it was two men to a package, then three, and four. Later, there were many more than that sharing the contents of one small parcel.

The next winter brought abject physical misery to the men. Fierce cold penetrated to the bones of the undernourished prisoners. The thought of food was never far away, and a man would spend hours daydreaming about what he would eat when freedom came.

John remembered the cock pheasant he had discovered in a poacher's trap while doing guard duty at the R.A.F. station in Scotland during the winter of 1940-1941. He had come upon it while plodding between some snow-laden trees, and decided it would make a good gift for his sister, Meriel, who was an officer in the South of England in the Women's Auxiliary Air Force. The mail usually took only a day or two to get there, so he wrapped it up carefully and sent it off.

Unfortunately, John Bull wasn't as prompt as usual in delivering mail, and the package, giving off a somewhat questionable odor, was delivered to her one week later. John wished now that he had eaten the bird himself. Every time he thought of it his mouth watered.

In spite of the deprivation and hardship, the morale of the prisoners remained high because of their knowledge that the Allies were winning the war.

One very important factor in keeping the morale high was American Flying Fortresses. Apparently the camp was on the route used by the U.S. Air Force in their daylight raids on Central and Eastern Germany. Day after day hundreds of Flying Fortresses, silver in the sunlight, would fly in perfect formation at an altitude of some 14,000 feet. The POW's would stand in the compound and cheer as they passed over on the way to their target, and again as they returned. To stop this manifestation of glee their captors began to herd them into the barracks each time the planes came over. They gave as the reason for doing this that it was dangerous for the prisoners to be in the open when enemy planes were overhead. So they must take shelter in the barracks.

Escape plans were almost continually underfoot in the camp. But they virtually came to an end when the camp commandant informed the prisoners that Hitler had given orders that all escaped POW's caught were to be shot.

The time came when they were told that the next Red

Cross food parcels would be the last. By this time they were down to one parcel to every 16 men. They were now totally dependent on the minimum rations given them by their captors. This ration was composed of one loaf of old bread a day divided among a dozen men and some thin vegetable soup. In addition there was the fish cheese. This once-scorned food was accepted now with alacrity. It was divided jealously and carefully, and was regarded as a great delicacy. The famished men began to scour the compound for weeds to eat. Edibles such as potato peelings were eagerly scavenged from the scrap heaps outside the two cookhouses in the camp were the German rations were prepared.

By now everybody in camp began to suffer from malnutrition. John began to experience alarming symptoms of numbness below the knees. Gradually, walking became difficult for him. He would stumble and fall when his foot struck even a small obstruction. He also began to notice that his sight was failing. He never fully recovered from this latter result of malnutrition, and even today wears heavy glasses.

Life now became only a dull existence with the satisfaction of hunger the strongest motivation. Men would drag themselves from their beds only when they had to.

Under these conditions the winter months of 1944-1945 crawled by apathetically.

Slowly spring came. With the sunlight and warmth, everybody began to perk up a bit. From the radio they had learned that the war could not continue much longer. They knew that their camp was not many miles from the Western Front, and wondered whether they would be evacuated once again. Aware of this possibility, John and Mason began to discuss what they would do if the camp were evacuated. They decided that, because Allied forces were bound to get to the camp in a matter of weeks, the thing to do was stay right where they were. But how?

As they discussed the matter, they concluded the best

thing to do was to hide in a hole under one of the barracks.

As at the other camp where John had been, the barracks were built about fifteen inches above the ground. This was enough space for the guards to look underneath.

There was one barracks where their stratagem might work. That building was near the gate of the compound. It was occupied by prisoners who had been put on parole by the German administration. They had signed paroles made according to International Law, by which they indicated they would not try to escape. They were performing duties outside the compound. These men had been granted permission to bank up earth around their barracks to keep the winter winds from blowing underneath and up through the cracks in the floor. Here was the ideal place for a hideaway pit.

John and Mason visited the barracks and asked its occupants for permission to carry out their plans and for their cooperation. The occupants agreed, but let them know they thought them crazy to try such a thing. Moreover, they reminded John and Mason that if they were caught they would probably be shot. But John pointed out to them that with his legs the way they were he couldn't possibly march, and stood a chance of being shot as a straggler in any case. He would rather take a chance of being caught trying to escape than almost surely being shot under other circumstances. They saw his point.

John and Mason began the preparation of their escape pit immediately. A few boards were removed underneath the table. Then they squeezed their way under the floor with their home-made digging tools, and the boards, table, and chairs were replaced.

The digging was done as quickly as possible, in shifts. The dirt was spread around over the ground in case a guard checked underneath with a flashlight. When they finished digging for the time being, they signaled, and the men above removed the boards and let them up. A special signal told them if a guard was around while they worked.

The pit was about six and a half feet long and two feet wide and deep. Bed boards were used to shore the sides and cover the top. The two of them, in essence, would be in a narrow box. A few boards were left off the top at one end so that they could wriggle through.

Because of their weakened condition it took them three days to finish the job. The day they finished the order came: The camp would be evacuated the next morning. That would be April 11, 1945.

Early in the morning scores of German guards marched into the camp, and the task of moving out 5,000 men began.

Barracks after barracks was emptied, their inhabitants lined up in the camp square, then marched through the gates flanked by their guards. Where were they going? None of the prisoners, at least, knew.

The evacuation began at the far end of the camp, which meant that the building under which John and Mason planned to hide would be evacuated last. They were very pleased at the way things were going. The fact that the barracks near the gate would be the last one emptied meant they would not have to spend extra hours cramped in the damp pit. The two of them collected the few essentials they would take into the pit with them and moved from barracks to barracks as each was emptied. In this way they kept just ahead of the proceedings.

Finally only three or four barracks remained to be evacuated. It was time to go down into the hideout.

As John slipped through the hole in the floor, someone said, "Well, mates, we wish you luck, but we think you're crazy. Is it worth it?"

"If we pull this off, we'll be celebrating the end of the war in London while you chaps are wandering around Germany."

Mason followed John into the darkness. As he disappeared the man who was to replace the floor boards observed, "I hope for your sakes the Jerries don't burn these buildings down so that the Allies can't have them."

"We'll have to take that chance," Mason replied.

As Mason squeezed through the hole he sprinkled pepper around on the ground near the pit in case the Germans sent dogs under the building to investigate. Lying on his back in the "box" he reached up and pulled as much dirt as he could over the boards, covering them. Then he moved the last boards into place, leaving a little space for air to enter. Then the two of them settled down as comfortably as they could in the cramped space and waited.

The main gate of the camp was only about one hundred feet away. They could hear the sound of men moving out from the barracks next door, the shouting guards, the rhythm of the prisoners' feet marching out in a continuous stream.

Then they heard the command of a German guard in the barracks above. The shuffling of feet over their heads told them that this last barracks was being emptied. The noise above lessened, then stopped.

Outside, the rhythm of marching feet continued. Then it, too, began to lessen, to recede. John listened as it grew farther away, and fainter and fainter. Then it ceased.

Eerie silence fell upon the camp. John had become used to continuous noise: the movement of feet; men talking, arguing, cursing; the creaking of beds at night; snoring. Now the silence was almost oppressive.

John and Mason lay still, hardly daring to move, their ears straining for any sound, for any smell: the smell of smoke, the crackling of fire, the sound of voices.

But the silence continued. Gradually, as the minutes passed, they began to relax.

"Looks as if we are safe so far," Mason observed.

"Consider Yourselves Liberated"

ANOTHER HOUR PASSED. It
would not pay to be in too much of a hurry;
no use to chance being caught.

The silence in the camp continued.

Finally John and Mason decided it was
time to investigate. As quietly as possible
they removed the cover boards, climbed
out of their pit, and wriggled through
the narrow space between the ground
and the floor above to the edge of the
barracks nearest the gate.

Lying on their stomachs side by side,
they carefully dug aside a little of the
soil piled around the building and peered
out.

"See any guards?" John inquired.

"Just a few POW's over there."

"Oh, yes! Probably the medical order-
lies the Jerries planned to leave behind
with the sick."

"Well, what do you think? Shall we
risk it?"

"We can't stay in this hole forever.
Might as well go now as later."

Digging away more of the dirt, they
crawled from under the building, stood
up, brushed themselves off, and began

walking toward the three or four POW's standing near the next barracks.

"Where did you fellows come from?" the men exclaimed when they saw the two.

Mason explained how they had hidden. They learned that two or three other prisoners also had managed to stay behind. A half dozen German guards had been left to watch the camp, but they were leaving the prisoners alone. They knew that the Allies would be arriving any day, and were not about to throw their weight around under such circumstances.

For a few minutes the group conjectured as to what might happen when the Allies arrived; then Mason asked about food. No food had been left in the camp for the POW's, they were told.

"Then let's go to the administration compound. There'll be some food left there for the guards," said Mason.

Painfully, John accompanied the others through the open gate into the administrative area. His legs didn't want to follow his commands, and he could not see clearly. A couple of guards watched them, but made no move to interfere.

In the cookhouse they found a storeroom stocked with food—bread, oatmeal, canned sauerkraut, canned meats—enough to feed the administration and guards for quite a while. There was enough food for all of them for some weeks. Apparently the departing Germans had not taken this food with them because they did not have sufficient transportation.

Finding some fuel, the ravenous men built a fire in the cookhouse stove, and soon the mouth-watering aroma of hot food filled the building. The temptation was to eat all they could hold. But they knew that their stomachs were not prepared for a full meal. And they could always eat again in a couple of hours.

With their physical needs supplied, they began to

discuss what ought to be done next. They finally decided that there was little point in leaving the camp. Where could they go? Besides, it was only a matter of time before their liberators would arrive.

Several days passed. One warm, sunny morning—it was April 15, 1945—John and Mason were sitting outside the doorway of the barracks nearest the main gate when prisoners standing near the gate began to shout excitedly and point.

Mason started to run toward them, with John following as best he could. Before John could get to the gate Mason turned to him and exclaimed, with deep emotion, "It's Monty's mob! It's Monty's mob! It's Monty's mob!"

He was referring to the men commanded by British Field Marshal Bernard Montgomery.

Grasping the wire fence between the barbs, John looked down the gently sloping hillside to the valley below. Through blurred eyes, blurred not only by faulty vision but also by unshed tears, he saw tank after khaki-colored tank rolling eastward in a long, ragged line. Clouds of dust billowed up behind them.

Then he heard the sound of deep sobs. One of the men had broken down completely. His thin frame shook as he leaned against one of the gateposts. His plane had been shot down and he had been captured in September, 1939, two or three days after the war had started. He had been a prisoner of war for five and one-half years.

After a time the emotional peak subsided, and everybody began talking, loudly, animatedly. Everybody was talking; nobody was listening. How soon they would be back home; what they were going to eat when they got there; what things were like now in London, Birmingham, Stockton-on-Tees, or wherever each man was from; what they were going to do now that the war was over.

Eventually they talked themselves out, and began to think of their immediate situation again. After a while

Through blurred eyes John saw a long, ragged line of tanks in the dust.

someone noticed that the German guards were not to be seen.

A few minutes later one of the POW's happened by the guardroom, and discovered that the guards had locked themselves inside. They had made themselves POW's in anticipation of the British Army taking over the camp.

Early in the afternoon there was a flurry of excitement at the gate separating the POW and administrative compounds. John and Mason arrived in time to see two armored cars painted in camouflage colors rolling across the administrative compound up to the gate. They stopped, the hatches on top of each were thrown back, and from each opening emerged the most beautiful faces John had ever seen. True, they were covered with the black grime of battle and a two- or three-day stubble covered their chins. But those men were more beautiful to John than was the angel that delivered Peter from prison.

A Cockney prisoner called out, "Where you from, mates?"

"The Seventh British Armored Division. We've been sent over here to liberate you chaps. So consider yourselves jolly well liberated," came the reply in a broad Scottish brogue that was lilting music to John's ears.

The conversation was being carried on through the barbed wire. But now the prisoners rushed through the gate, just so that they could touch the cars. In tears, the man who had been a prisoner for five and a half years bent over and kissed one of the dusty vehicles.

By now the four men in the two cars had climbed out. The dozen or so prisoners crowded around them. There was much laughing, hugging, back slapping, shaking of hands, and questions.

"What about the war?" one of the POW's asked.

"Oh, it's just about over. It won't be long before we'll be shaking the hands of the Ruskies."

Mason turned to John. He was dressed the same way John had seen him hundreds of times before. But there was something about the occasion that impressed his appearance indelibly upon John's memory. He stood there, a huge man in spite of his loss of weight, a faded R.A.F. uniform hanging loosely about him. His black-bearded face was topped with a brown woolen cap like an old-fashioned nightcap, which he wore all the time to protect his bald head. A huge grin split his face through the beard. He gripped John's hand hard and said with an emotion that caused his voice to quiver, "Well, fellow, we made it. We got away."

No longer prisoners, the group were now free to move around as they wished. It would take a while before the British could take over and get matters organized so that they could be sent back to England.

Two weeks passed before John was flown back to England, on April 29, 1945. A new uniform, an officer's, was issued to him. Accumulated seniority gave him the rank of Flight Lieutenant. After a medical checkup and treatment, he was given leave and sent home.

With the jubilant crowd at Picadilly Circus John celebrated V-E Day.

John's father met him when he got off the train at Ruislip, the station nearest his home. They met in the middle of the footbridge over the tracks. John put down his bags, and they looked at each other for a moment. Then they were in each other's arms.

Together they walked to the bus stop. John had to use his hands to lift his weakened legs up to the bus step. As he climbed aboard, the passengers began to applaud. They realized he was a prisoner of war, among the first to return home.

On May 8, 1945, V-E (Victory in Europe) Day was announced. The war in Europe was over.

John caught the crowded underground and rode into London that day. At Picadilly Circus he allowed himself to be carried along with the jubilant, singing, shouting crowds celebrating the end of long, grim, costly struggle.

He remembered his words to the POW as he squeezed through the floor into the hideaway pit: "If we pull this off, we'll be celebrating the end of the war in London while you chaps are wandering around Germany."

Now he was celebrating the war's end in London. He wondered where those 5,000 men were at the moment.

It was not until some years later that he found out.

One day he was reading a *Reader's Digest* when he came across a story of several thousand British prisoners of war with their guards who had wandered around Germany for several weeks before the end of the war. As he read along he came across the name of a man he knew —Warrant Officer Dixie Dean. *That was the name of the senior man in John's prisoner-of-war camp.*

With intense interest John read how the army of ragged, hungry men had moved about, scavenging off the land to stay alive. On one occasion they had been attacked with rockets and antipersonnel bombs by nine R.A.F. fighters, whose pilots thought they were a German army. Sixty men had been killed outright; others died later of wounds. Grimly he thought of how close he had come to being among that unhappy army.

With his health restored, John made up his mind to stay in the Royal Air Force, provided he could fly. However, he was told that his eyes disqualified him for flying. He was offered a position as a transportation officer but decided not to accept and to resign from the R.A.F.

He got a job with a construction company, drawing blueprints. Then his interest turned to building construction. He decided to specialize in reinforced concrete roofing, and make construction his lifework. With this in mind he began to take a night course on the subject.

John after his liberation from the POW camp and his return to England.

But as time went on he began to feel restless and unsettled. His father, who had been watching him through the months, decided that his son needed something to snap him out of that condition. About this time he learned through a friend that a London firm that owned tea plantations in North India was looking for an assistant to the manager for one of them. Knowing John's interest in adventure, he suggested to his friend that perhaps John would be interested.

In due time John received an invitation to accept the position. It took only a little thought to decide he would like it.

In October, 1946, he sailed away from London for India and for a new and quite different life than he had known.

The leisurely trip across the Mediterranean Sea, through the Suez Canal, and across the Arabian Sea to Bombay was a pleasant one for John. He felt ready for whatever adventures the future held for him.

Of Tigers, Temperance, and a Sunday Afternoon

THE BORDERS OF India and Bangladesh (formerly East Pakistan) meet at the head of the Bay of Bengal and continue together up to the Himalayan kingdom of Nepal. But just as the northwestern finger of Bangladesh and the southeastern finger of Nepal are about to touch, a narrow neck of Indian land interposes and thwarts the meeting. Following through this isthmus on a map one is surprised to find Indian territory spreading east and south once more. It continues some 600 miles northeast, to end at the conjunction of the borders of China and Burma, and follows southward the eastern border of Bangladesh and the western borders of Burma almost to the Bay of Bengal.

This area, which approaches twice the size of Bangladesh, is made up of the North East Frontier Agency, the territories of Manipur and Tripura, and the states of Assam and West Bengal. It is this last state, which is bordered on the north by the tiny nation of Sikkim and the larger country of Bhutan, that one enters when he travels across the land link from India proper.

141

From the train window John could see the rugged Himalayan foothills.

John's journey ended in West Bengal at the tea plantation of the Needern Tea Company at Dalsingpara, at the end of the railway line. The plantation was only three miles south of the Bhutan frontier, on the fringes of the Himalayan foothills. He had traveled by train across India, from Bombay to Calcutta, where he spent a day or two visiting the company's main office in India and seeing the city. An eighteen-hour train trip through what is now Bangladesh (the separation of India and Pakistan would take place the next year) had brought him to Dalsingpara early in the morning.

Looking out of his carriage window as his train drew near to Dalsingpara, John could see the rugged Himalayan foothills, which marked the Bhutan border, rising abruptly from the jungled plains. The early morning sun slanting across the trees and falling on range after range of hills rising one after another to the distant mountains presented a prospect of peace and beauty.

When the train pulled into the little station John caught sight of a white face among the dark Indian faces on the platform. As he stepped down from the carriage onto the platform following a coolie carrying his bags, the white man approached him. "I suppose you're John Curnow," he said in a thick Scottish brogue.

The tall, thin man introduced himself as Bobby Toms, the manager of the tea estate of which John was to be assistant.

As they drove along, Bobby told John something about the estate. It covered an area of 4,000 acres, 1,350 of which were under tea. Some 1,800 people were employed there, picking tea, working in the processing factory, and maintaining the estate.

An Indian stepped out into the road about one hundred yards ahead and waved. Bobby stepped on the brakes.

"Sahib, a tiger has killed a cow two miles up the road. Could you come and shoot the tiger?"

"I'll try. Build a *macchan* [tree platform]."

"It is already done."

"What is the best time to go?"

"Get onto the *macchan* at four o'clock, sahib."

Bobby looked at John. "Game on starting your stint in India by hunting tigers?"

"Sure," John answered.

The administrative bungalow of the estate was close to the road. Roofed verandas ran the full width of the building, back and front. Inside the building were three offices—a large one for the office staff and two smaller ones for the manager and his assistant.

Behind the administrative building was the two-storied tea factory. Near the factory was the three-storied weathering shed where the leaves were dried. Some two hundred Indian men worked in the complicated process of preparing the tea, which was finally graded and packed into large tin-foil-lined plywood boxes.

The bungalows of the manager and his assistant were set in a clearing in the trees to one side of the factory.

At twenty minutes to four an employee brought the car to Bobby's bungalow. A few miles down the road two men signaled them. As they drew to a stop, John could see the dead cow lying near the right side of the road. On the other side a platform about four and one-half feet square was hidden among the leaves of a tree some thirteen feet from the ground. The men helped John and Bobby up onto the platform, and passed Bobby's double-barreled 405 rifle up to him. After arranging to return in a couple of hours the three of them climbed into the car and drove off.

"Now, John, we've got to be absolutely quiet and not move a hair. We don't want that tiger up here in our laps. Keep your eyes open. If you see him, give a little hiss."

Squatting on the small platform peering through the leaves, John began to feel rather vulnerable. Thirteen feet was not very high, he began to think.

The minutes ticked by. Some twenty had passed when Bobby gave a soft hiss. Slowly John turned his head so that he could see the dead cow. Sitting three or four yards from it was a massive tiger.

A feeling of admiration came over John as he gazed at the great yellow-and-black cat. It would be a shame to destroy such strength and beauty, he thought. But it was necessary. Once a tiger had begun killing cattle it would continue the practice.

Slowly Bobby raised his rifle and took aim. He can't miss at this range, John thought.

The rifle crashed. The tiger uttered a ground-shaking roar, sprang upward, and disappeared into the jungle.

"Well, what have we got on our hands now?" Bobby wondered aloud.

He went on to explain that a wounded tiger is a tremendous menace. If it is incapacitated so that it cannot hunt its natural prey, it becomes a mankiller. For that reason it must be hunted down and dispatched.

After a wait of five minutes to be sure the tiger wouldn't come back, they climbed down from the platform and crossed to where it had been sitting. There was no blood on the ground. Watchfully, they followed the direction the animal had taken. There was no sign of blood. Bobby had missed entirely.

John was astonished that he had failed at such close range. It seemed to him that the rankest novice could have hit a target that was so close up.

That night Bobby took John to a club where overseas men from the several plantations in the area got together. John was introduced to the men, one of whom had a withered left arm. After a while the conversation got around to tigers and tiger hunting. The man with the lame arm told his story.

He had been hunting tigers by elephant. Several hunters and elephants were involved. A tiger, cornered, had been wounded by one of the hunters. The storyteller on his elephant driven by a mahout had been close to the wounded animal. In its pain and fury it had come straight at his elephant, sprung on its back, knocked the man off, and jumped on top of him. Then it proceeded to chew on his arm.

Both the mahout and the elephant remained calm. Quickly the mahout turned the elephant about. Then the massive beast placed one of its great feet upon the tiger without touching the tea planter. The man rolled away, and the elephant coolly crushed the tiger to death.

Two evenings later John visited another club, some eighteen miles from his plantation. There he met a planter with an artificial leg. This man told him he had lost his leg when a tiger had sprung up to the *macchan* where he and a companion had been waiting for it. It

began to maul him, and he would have been killed but
for his companion.

John now realized why Bobby had missed. Before
hearing these stories he thought he could have calmly
shot the animal, because he had done well on the range
while in the R.A.F. Now were he called upon to shoot
one he might well miss from nervousness.

John worked as an assistant manager out on the estate while another, senior man, was assistant manager in
the factory. In four or five months he had learned Hindustani well enough to communicate with the workers,
although it was about a year before he could speak the
language fluently.

As the months and years passed, John became ab-
sorbed in his work. Three and a half years of service en-
titled him to a six-month furlough, which he planned to
take in the summer of 1950. However, in 1949 Bobby
Toms resigned and another manager, Jack Edge, took his
place. Edge had spent some time in India and was due
for furlough at the same time. Consequently, John agreed
to take his furlough six months early in order to be on the
job while Edge was away.

After four and a half months in England visiting with
his parents and friends he booked passage back to India
in February, 1950, on the P. and O. luxury liner the
S.S. *Canton,* which was on the way to Hong Kong.

Three days out from London the ship was sailing
through a calm Mediterranean Sea. There was a snap in
the air, and John was taking his exercise around the deck.
As he walked he noticed a very attractive Chinese girl.

On John's next turn she smiled at him. The next
time around he stopped and introduced himself. He
found her to be a very intelligent, interesting girl. In a
short time they were spending all their days together.

Her name was Wang Mei-li. Her father had been a
high-ranking official of Canton Province in China during
the Chiang Kai-shek regime.

When the ship reached Bombay after a two-and-a-half-week trip, there was mutual regret at the parting. They promised to write each other regularly.

In one of the letters that John received from her about a year later Mei-li told him she was flying to England to attend college, and would stop off at Calcutta. She would send him a telegram informing him just when she would be in the city.

In about three weeks the telegram came. John flew down to Calcutta and spent two days with her. When she boarded her plane for London they were engaged.

Saturday was always club day for the tea-estate managers. During the afternoon the men would play tennis. After dinner in the evening they would sit in the bar drinking, playing cards, and talking.

It was midnight on a Saturday night. All the married men had gone home, and only the five bachelors in the group were left drinking and talking.

The conversation drifted around to a tea estate manager named Hayworth, whose wife was in England while their children were in school.

Hayworth had developed the habit of staying in his bungalow drinking by himself. That was bad, they all agreed. When a man begins drinking by himself he is an alcoholic.

"It's all very well for us to criticize that fellow," one of them spoke up. "But what about us? We're alcoholics too."

Indignant sounds greeted his words.

"Well, we wouldn't sit here so often drinking till after midnight if we weren't alcoholics."

The words struck John hard. He was aware that he was drinking more than he should. But an alcoholic!

He turned to the speaker and held up his glass of whisky and soda, two thirds full. "Are you telling me I'm under the control of this stuff? That I can't give it up when I want to?"

"Sure, you're under its control."

"If that's what you think I'll show you I'm not under the control of this stuff." He pushed his glass across the table. "I won't touch it again."

Although he kept going to the club, he never again drank.

John had also been smoking heavily, from forty to fifty cigarettes a day. One morning his bearer came in to awaken him with his *pulling ka char* ("bedside tea"), as was the custom. John took a sip, then as usual lighted a cigarette. When he took the first draw, it tasted bitter. With a grimace he snuffed it out. Late in the afternoon it occurred to him that he had not had the urge to smoke all day. He never lighted another cigarette.

How the urge had disappeared was a puzzle to him. He had tried on several previous occasions to quit but could not.

Sunday evenings John liked to relax alone in his bungalow reading and listening to the radio. The station he generally tuned to was Radio Ceylon. It played the type of easy listening music he enjoyed.

Each Sunday evening at nine o'clock the station would announce a program called the Voice of Prophecy. John knew that it was a religious program, so he would tune in to another station.

One Sunday evening in late November, 1951, he was reading as usual with the music from Radio Ceylon providing a soft background. He was so immersed in his book that he did not notice it was nine o'clock. Suddenly his attention was caught by a song. The song ended, and a man began to speak. His pleasant voice and conversational style appealed to John, so he listened to the whole program and found himself enjoying it.

The next Sunday evening he deliberately left the radio tuned to Radio Ceylon when nine o'clock came. In a few weeks he found himself looking forward to the program.

One Sunday evening as the King's Heralds were singing "There is a place of quiet rest, Near to the heart of God," John found his heart strangely moved. Then H. M. S. Richards began to quote the chorus, as the quartet hummed in the background:

O Jesus, blest Redeemer,
    Sent from the heart of God,
Hold us, who wait before Thee,
    Near to the heart of God.

As he was speaking, the Holy Spirit came upon John with overwhelming conviction. He felt that he was a great sinner before God. A tremendous longing for forgiveness and inner peace took possession of him.

Suddenly he found himself upon his knees in front of the radio pouring out his heart to God. As he confessed his sins a wonderful peace filled his heart. Peace and light, like the breaking of a glorious dawn. John realized for the first time that he had been living for a long, long time in the darkness and thralldom of sin. But now he was free!

From that time John Curnow was a different man, living up to all the light he had.

Seventeen years later an Adventist missionary was Ingathering at the tea plantations of West Bengal when he met a planter who had known John before he became an Adventist.

"How is Curnow doing?" the planter asked.

The missionary told him that at the time he was principal of the Lowry Memorial School in South India.

"You people sure changed that fellow," the planter remarked. Then he went on to say that John Curnow had been considered one of the most blasphemous men around and that the change in his life had made a tremendous impression on the planters.

John continued to listen to the Voice of Prophecy for another month. Then he decided that he ought to begin taking the Bible correspondence course it offered. He wrote to the Voice of Prophecy Bible School in Poona, and in a week or so received two lessons of an introductory Bible course.

Then he discovered that he needed a Bible to study the course, so he wrote back and asked them to send him one.

It took him almost two years to finish the first course. Sometimes weeks went by without his studying at all. But he never missed listening to the Voice of Prophecy program each Sunday evening.

The plantation had had a new manager each year since 1949. In April, 1952, George Forrest, the fourth manager since John had been with the estate, went to England on furlough. John was appointed acting manager.

Trouble on the Plantation

ONE SUNDAY EVENING H. M. S. Richards answered questions during the radio program. One of the questions was "To what denomination do you belong?"

"I am an ordained minister of the Seventh-day Adventist Church," was the answer.

Several days later Max Warner, the manager of a nearby plantation, dropped by for a visit. During the course of the conversation the subject got around to religion, and John mentioned that the Voice of Prophecy to which he was listening was a Seventh-day Adventist program.

"What's that?"

"I don't really know."

After a while Warner left. But John was surprised to see his car drive up again a half hour later.

"Say, Curnow," he exclaimed, as he came into John's bungalow, "those people you are studying with: They don't use alcohol or tobacco. And they don't drink coffee—or tea. Did you know that?"

"Where did you get that from?"

"I looked it up in my encyclopedia."

151

"What has tea or coffee got to do with religion?"

"You've got me! Ask them!"

This information deeply disturbed John. That evening he sat down and wrote a rather perplexed letter to Poona, asking why Seventh-day Adventists did not drink tea.

Many months later he learned that his letter had put the Voice of Prophecy staff in Poona in a dither. John had taken only six lessons at the time, and they did not want to alienate him at that stage. So a very careful answer was sent off by A. E. Rawson, the Voice of Prophecy departmental secretary, which pointed out some of the ill effects of tea but did not press the point of abstinence. When John read the letter the question of tea became a dead issue in his mind. Adventists' belief regarding tea did not seem to affect his career, so he forgot about it.

With his new job of acting manager John inherited a number of problems. The biggest one was labor unrest. For various reasons the plantation had had four managers in four years. The frequent changing and the uncertainty that went with it weakened the managerial authority on the estate and engendered dissatisfaction in the minds of the workers.

The problems were greatly aggravated by a militant trade union that had managed to get a foothold on the plantation. By the time John became acting manager this union, which was only a minority among the workers, was stirring up a great deal of trouble by intimidation of the laborers, by promises, and by fiery speeches by the leaders.

There was also a lot of tension between this union and a larger, more moderate group that had become established on the estate. In particular the militants wanted to get rid of Rajaman, one of the two chief Indian supervisors on the plantation, who was also the leader of the moderate group.

In the face of these problems the time would come

Women plucking tea leaves on the plantation that John was managing.

when John would have to establish his authority on the estate. It was obvious that there was going to be a confrontation with the militants.

A few days after John became acting manager he was sitting at his desk about noontime. His assistant, Dave Waters, was away. As he was working on some papers he began to notice that a lot of animated talking was going on outside. Stepping out onto the back veranda to investigate, he found that some one hundred men had gathered between the office and the tea factory. He recognized them as the militant labor group.

"*Kia mangta hai* ["What do you want"] ?" he asked.

All began talking at the same time.

John raised his hand. "Let one man speak."

One stepped from the group. John recognized him as

a very unpleasant demagogic fellow named Lal.
Feeling his importance, Lal swaggered forward.
"You must get rid of Rajaman," he demanded. "He
ill-treats the women laborers. He is not fit to be employed. He must be fired."
John knew that the accusations about Rajaman were
not true. He also knew that he must be extremely cau-
tious. The mob could turn violent, and then there was
no knowing what might happen.
He could give in to their demands, but he knew that
if he did this, he was beaten. He might as well pack up
his bags and go, for he would have no more authority. But
he could not say a blunt "No!" The temper of his con-
fronters would not take that.
Praying earnestly for help, he tried to persuade them.
"Oh, Rajaman isn't that bad. You don't really want me to
fire him."
The talk went back and forth for almost an hour but
was getting nowhere. Finally John decided to go back to
his office. But when he made the move, Lal, the leader of
the mob, told him to stay on the veranda. The look in the
man's eyes told him he had better comply.
During the talking the men had crowded around the
steps leading onto the veranda. Now, impatient that they
were getting nowhere, they began to be more hostile.
Some of them began to crowd onto the veranda behind
Lal, who was already there.
Should they come on the veranda, that would put
John in a more dangerous situation than he was already
in, he realized. He began to bluff. Taking an authoritative
attitude, he walked toward them. "Get down! Lal is your
representative; I will talk to him."
Feeling complimented, Lal said, "Yes, I will talk to
sahib. You stay down."
None of them tried to come onto the veranda after that.
Again the talking began. There would be periods of
loud talking by Lal or one of the others. Then John would

patiently try to answer their arguments. Sometimes there were long, strained periods of silence. John wondered what the outcome of the whole thing was going to be.

Five hours passed. In a short time it would be dark. John prayed earnestly in his heart.

Suddenly he saw John Tebbutt. Tebbutt had been an assistant on the estate but had recently transferred to a neighboring estate, where he was acting manager. He had driven up and parked his car on the other side of the administrative bungalow, so John hadn't seen him come. He had walked through the office onto the back veranda where John was standing.

John could see that he had grasped the situation at a glance. But he spoke very casually in Hindustani, "What's it all about?"

Equally casually John waved his hand toward the men. *"Kuch ne! Kalli bhatchit korta hai* ["Nothing. We're only talking"]."

Then he added quietly in English, "It's serious! Do something!"

Tebbutt glanced at his watch. "You're busy," he said in Hindustani. "I can't wait. I'll see you later."

Nonchalantly he went back through the bungalow, and John heard him drive off.

Inwardly he breathed a deep sigh of relief. What if the mob had not allowed Tebbutt to leave?

The haranguing began again. How long can this go on without something breaking? John wondered wearily. He knew it would be at least an hour before Tebbutt could get back with the police. Would the mob's patience snap before that time?

Now Lal began to lose his temper. He would come close to John, who by now was standing with his back to the wall, and would shout at him incoherently for a minute or two while literally frothing at the mouth. Then John would quietly try to reason with him while the others listened, adding their arguments now and then.

An hour passed. Then an hour and a half. The tension could be felt. "God, bring the police soon!" John prayed. "This situation can't go on much longer."

Now it was nine o'clock. Suddenly there was a shout from the group. *"Police ay-gia* ["Police have come"]!" They began to run toward the front of the building, where the police were.

Quickly John went into the bungalow, to meet Tebbutt coming through. "Sorry I'm late, John. I'll explain later."

Now a tremendous shout went up from the front of the building. Going to the front door, John and Tebbutt saw two constables with crossed rifles blocking the door while the mob tried to push through. A third man, a sergeant, was endeavoring to reason with them.

It was an hour before things finally cooled off and the mob dispersed, after agreeing to talk things over with John and the police next morning.

After they had gone John wiped his brow and turned to Tebbutt. "Man, you got here just in time. What took you so long?"

"Sorry, old boy! The police were away on patrol. I had to go out and find them."

When John and the police met with the dissidents the next morning Lal and his group had lost their initiative. The police warned them not to cause any more trouble, and John promised not to bring any disciplinary action against them. Things quieted down for a while.

The tea-plucking season began in May and continued until October. Another incident took place in September. A plucking force of some one thousand men and women were out daily gathering the small leaves, which they would bring in to the weighing station at the factory. The leaves were carried in large baskets slung on the back and suspended by straps worn around the head over the forehead.

Weighing was done several times a day. There was a

final weighing about four o'clock in the afternoon.

One afternoon Dave Waters, John's assistant, had come in from the tea fields, and John and he made their way to the leaf-weighing shed for the final weighing. Ordinarily the men and women came in, had their tea weighed, had the amount credited to them in a book, and went on their way. John had information that the reactionary union was planning to bring matters to a head again. The comparatively short picking season, when time was of the essence, would be a strategic opportunity for them. He had expected trouble any day. Immediately, John knew this was the day. The workers were not weighing in, but were silently waiting.

In a few minutes Rajaman and the other supervisors arrived. They advised John to say nothing and not to ask the pickers why they were not weighing in.

At the end of twenty minutes all the one thousand pickers had crowded around the weighing shed, the women in a group by themselves. The silence was electric with tension. John and Waters stood about fifty feet from the station watching the proceedings. They had agreed that if serious trouble seemed imminent, they would go to the veranda, where they could face the mob with their backs to the wall. They did not want to be surrounded.

Suddenly a group among the men began to shout. They began to move from the weighing shed toward John and Waters.

"This looks like it," he said to Waters. "Let's get to the office."

They turned and began to walk at an unhurried pace toward the administrative bungalow.

The shouting took on a higher, shriller pitch. John could hear the sound of many bare feet running toward them. The mob would be upon them in seconds.

But for Waters and him to run would be to lose all prestige and authority.

"Let's stop," John said.

They halted and swung around. The mob of some
one hundred men, about twenty-five feet behind them,
came to a stop. The shouting died.

It was a moment of high drama. There stood two lone
men facing an angry mob, while hundreds of tea pickers
watched with intense interest. And from the windows of
the tea factory hundreds of other eyes peered at the scene
taking place before them. Almost the whole working
force of the plantation was witnessing the confrontation.

John stood feet apart, hands on hips, leaning slightly
forward. He chose one man and looked him in the eye
steadily, unblinkingly, until his eyes dropped. Then he
looked at another man, and another. Waters was following
his example.

All the time John was praying. He asked for self-
control; that his anxiety would not show on his face; for
help in overcoming the trouble. He reminded God that
he had tried to run the plantation on a Christian basis,
considering the welfare of both the company and the
workers. He believed that the influence at work on the estate from the dissident union was an evil one, and he
asked for help that it might be overcome. He prayed that
the employees on the estate, who now knew that he was a
Christian, would see the influence of true Christianity.

After several minutes the mob of men began to shuffle
in embarrassment, not able to look the two men in
the eye.

At last John felt that they were cowed. "Come on.
Let's go!"

They turned away. Immediately the mob started to
run toward them, shouting.

Without having taken a step John and Waters swung
back to face them. By now the men were only about a
dozen feet away.

Tight-lipped and stern-faced, John and Waters began
again to stare at the men, whose gaze kept dropping

before them. This time John was determined to stare them down until they were completely demoralized and to have all the watching workers see their demoralization.

Silently the two looked from face to face, minute after minute. In a few minutes the men were not only shuffling but some of them were forced to turn their backs. Still John and Waters continued to look unblinkingly.

The mob became noticeably more and more cowed. But John and Waters continued to gaze steadily at them. At last it was evident that there was a collapse of morale in the group. Out of the corner of his eye John could see that some of the watchers were becoming amused at the embarrassment of the men.

"Come on. Now we *can* go," he stated.

They walked away. Only silence followed their going.

In John's heart was great thankfulness to God for overriding in such a desperate situation. There was also elation. For he knew that because the leaders of the trouble-making union had been so signally humiliated and discredited before practically the entire estate their influence was broken. He was right. From that day until he left the plantation eighteen months later he had nothing but peaceable, amiable relationships with his laborers.

A short time later George Forrest resigned while still on furlough in England and John was made manager.

And So They Were Married

IN HIS LETTERS to Mei-li in England, John began to write about his new-found faith in Jesus. At first she took it with tolerance and amusement. But as he continued to write in the same vein, her attitude changed, until her letters began to show antagonism toward him. Finally she asked John to stop mentioning Jesus Christ in his letters.

Meanwhile, John had written to A. E. Rawson in Poona explaining his relationship to Mei-li, mentioning that she had a Buddhist background and asking advice. A sympathetic letter came back. But in it was pointed out that Christians should not be "unequally yoked together."

This letter helped John to make up his mind that if she would not come along with him in his experience with Jesus he would have to break with her. He finally wrote her telling her he could not stop writing about Jesus. And if she still insisted that he do so, he would not expect to receive another letter from her. He never did.

In October, 1953, he received a letter from Poona telling him that H. M. S.

Richards would be visiting India, and that a Voice of Prophecy rally would be held in Calcutta in November. Would he be able to attend?

John arranged to take a two-week vacation so that he could be in Calcutta to meet Elder Richards.

The Voice of Prophecy rally was scheduled to be held on a Friday evening and Sabbath. It was with keen anticipation that John arrived in Calcutta on Friday afternoon and, after finding a hotel room, drove by taxi to 36 Park Street where the church is. It would be his first visit to a Seventh-day Adventist church and the first time he would meet a Seventh-day Adventist.

It was an exhilarating experience for John when he stood before the tall bespectacled man whose voice was so familiar to him, to grip his hand and to experience the warm, engaging personality. He was happy, too, to meet A. E. Rawson, whose letters from Poona had done much to help and encourage him.

The Friday evening and Sabbath meetings were gratifying to John. He was sorry that they were so soon over.

On Saturday night Elder Rawson asked John what his plans were for the rest of his vacation. John had thought of going to Puri, a Hindu temple town in the State of Orissa, where there was a fine beach.

Rawson explained that he had to fly with Elder Richards to East Pakistan the next day but that he would be returning to Calcutta on Monday while Elder Richards flew on to Burma. "Why don't you wait here until Monday, then go with me to Poona for the rest of your vacation?"

The idea appealed to John. He agreed.

John enjoyed his stay at Poona's Salisbury Park, the estate on which is situated the headquarters of the Southern Asia Division. He met Robert H. Pierson, who was the division president at the time; Martin E. Kemmerer, division treasurer; and other friendly, helpful people. Elder and Mrs. Rawson were his hosts on the estate.

While John was in Poona he made his decision to become a Seventh-day Adventist.

In four months he would be on his way home to England for furlough. He decided to stop at Poona at that time and be baptized. He would finish the Voice of Prophecy advanced course in the months before his furlough.

At Poona he learned that there was a Seventh-day Adventist school, Raymond Memorial School, at Falakata, only twenty-five miles from Dalsingpara. On his first Sabbath back on the plantation he drove to the school. The principal was Lennie Hare, son of Eric B. Hare, the Dr. Rabbit of Burma fame.

From that time on, for the three months that were left to John before he would leave for England, he went to Falakata almost every Sabbath. A warm friendship developed between him and Lennie, and Lennie's wife, Esther.

On John's last visit to the Hares, when he was saying good-by, Lennie said, "Now, John, you be sure to bring back a nice wife."

In Poona, John was baptized in the Salisbury Park church. Before he left to catch his ship at Bombay, Elder Rawson gave him a letter of introduction to C. R. Bonney, the Voice of Prophecy secretary for the British Union, and said smilingly, "When you come back, bring back a nice wife with you."

The trip across the Arabian Sea, up the Red Sea, and into the Mediterranean, was a pleasant one. The last port of call before London was Marseilles, in Southern France.

It was afternoon when John's ship sailed away from Marseilles and turned toward Gibraltar. The spring sun was shining brightly and the sea was like a mirror. John leaned over the railing for a while, then went down to his cabin. It was somewhere in this vicinity that I met Mei-li just about four years ago, he thought.

After hearing the Voice of Prophecy, John became a Seventh-day Adventist. In 1972 he visited H. M. S. Richards at VOP headquarters.

Although he hadn't written to or heard from Mei-li for more than a year, he still had several large photographs she had given him. He took them from his suitcase and looked at them a moment. Then he went to the open porthole of his cabin and spun them, one by one, into the water. He watched as they were caught in the slip stream and carried away. Then he turned and knelt by his bed in prayer.

"Lord, I've followed Your commandment not to be unequally yoked. After my furlough I'll be going back to India for another four years. Lord, You know I'm thirty years old and need a companion to take back to India with me. I'm leaving it up to You. I believe You have kept a girl for me. Bring us together."

Three days later his ship docked in London. His two sisters, Barbara and Meriel, met him, and went with him to his mother's house. His father had died while he was in India.

There was some making right John thought he had to do while in England.

After John, Mason, and the few other prisoners of war at the Sulingen prison camp had been liberated by the men of the Seventh British Army Division, a week or more passed before it could be arranged for them to be taken from there and flown to England.

Because of the disorganization the freed prisoners were on their own for a few days until the British Army was able to send in some men to take over the camp and to bring in other freed men who were to be sent back to England. In the interim John and Mason had decided to "liberate" some things from the Germans. After all, hadn't the Germans taken their possessions, including John's pen and his expensive Omega watch?

Consequently, Mason had "liberated" a rifle and a couple of bicycles. However, John's weak legs had made it difficult for him to ride a bicycle. So they "liberated" a large motorcycle, on which they cycled over the countryside enjoying themselves. During that time John had relieved some Germans of two cameras—a Leica and an Agfa—and a pair of Zeiss binoculars.

Now John went to the German legation in London and returned the cameras and binoculars. When he explained his reason for doing so the legate smiled understandingly. He had had many other men come to him for the same reason.

A few days after his arrival home John caught a bus from Ickenham, where his mother was living, to Watford, some fifteen miles away. There he called at the British Union Conference office at Stanborough Park. He gave Elder Rawson's letter of introduction to C. R. Bonney, and was cordially received.

Before John left, he asked Elder Bonney which church he would suggest he attend the next Sabbath.

"Why don't you come here to the Stanborough Park church? You will meet more young people here than at some of our other churches."

A few people smiled at John during Sabbath school and church at Stanborough Park on Sabbath, but nobody spoke to him. The church service over, John left the church with the others and stood outside, uncertain what to do.

After a few moments a young man came up to him and extended his hand. "I'm Mervyn Whiting. I believe you are a visitor to our church."

Mervyn was about twenty-four years old, a friendly fellow of medium height with a shock of light-brown wavy hair.

John told him his name and explained that he had just come back from India and had been baptized a day or so before leaving there.

Mervyn took John home to lunch and to meet his bride of just two months. They spent a pleasant afternoon together.

The next Sabbath John was invited by Mervyn and

Iris to attend another church. In the evening John and
Mervyn attended an MV meeting being held at the Stanborough church an hour before sundown.

When the service was over, Mervyn said, "How about
meeting some young people?"

Mervyn looked around. Over to one side of the church
was a group of four or five young men and women talking. Mervyn took John over.

"Joan," Mervyn called.

One of the girls turned toward them.

"Joan. I want you to meet John Curnow. He's just
come home from India on furlough. John, this is Joan
Gallaher."

John couldn't quite understand why, but as he
stepped forward to shake her hand she seemed just the
slightest bit flustered. Later he learned the reason for it.
Over John's shoulder Mervyn had given Joan a big meaningful wink, as if to say, "Here's a chap for you! It's up
to you now!" Joan was the only one of the circle of
friends who was not married.

They talked for a few minutes. Then Joan said, "Sorry,
I must run along. We are going Ingathering."

John asked Mervyn about her as casually as he could.
He learned that she was a registered nurse and midwife,
and that her father was a physiotherapist at the Stanbor-
oughs Hydro, the Seventh-day Adventist sanitarium at
Stanborough Park.

The next Sabbath John made sure that he met Joan
again. He found her talking to some friends in the foyer
of the church. He asked her how she had done at Ingathering the week before, and learned that she was going
out again that night.

It wasn't until the next Sabbath that they met again.
During the church service an announcement was made
that there were still a few seats available on a bus that had
been chartered to take people to the graduation at Newbold College the next day.

"It would be nice if you could attend the Newbold graduation," Joan remarked. "Do you plan to go?"

"Are you going on the bus?" John asked.

"Yes," Joan smiled.

"Could I go with you?"

"Yes." Was there a note of enthusiasm in that response, John wondered, or was it just his imagination? Joan said she would arrange for him to have one of the seats still available.

The bus, which would start from Watford, would pass within two miles of John's mother's home. He could meet the bus on the road. They arranged to sit together.

As the bus drew to a halt where John was standing the next morning he was conscious of curious eyes looking at him through its windows, and of eighty eyes following him as he made his way down the bus and took the only vacant seat left, the one next to Joan.

John was impressed with the service at Newbold. He was even more impressed by the girl he was accompanying. He found her a vivacious, interesting companion.

On the way back from the college Joan mentioned that because the next weekend would be a long one, Monday being a holiday, a group of young people from the Stanborough church were planning to camp out by the Thames River. John said that he liked camping, and asked whether she was going.

She was. Would he be interested in joining the group?

And so John found himself with a group of some twenty young people in tents at a place called Wallingford on the Thames from Friday afternoon until Monday afternoon. He and Joan spent a lot of time together that weekend.

Monday evening they traveled back to Watford together on the chartered bus. When he took her home that evening they were engaged.

John had not yet met Joan's parents. During the three weeks he and Joan had known each other Mr. and Mrs.

Returning to England by ship in early 1954, John prayed that he'd find a good wife. That summer he met and married Joan Gallaher.

Gallaher were away on vacation. In one or two of her letters to them Joan had casually referred to a chap named John Curnow from India, who was attending church. Now she was to be married to this fellow about whom her parents knew practically nothing.

John arranged to be with Joan when her parents arrived back from their vacation. After being introduced, he helped Mr. Gallaher unload the car while Joan followed her mother into the kitchen. As Mrs. Gallaher bustled around unpacking, Joan tried to find words to break the news to her. Her mother would be furious, she feared.

"Mother, what do you think of John?" she asked hesitatingly.

"Oh, he seems a nice young man."

There was a pause, then in fear and trembling Joan said, "Mother!"

"Yes, dear?" Mrs. Gallaher had picked up a basket and was taking some dishes from it.

"Mother—John and I are engaged."

"Isn't that wonderful!"

"Mother, I'm going to have to go to India with him."

"How marvelous!"

And that was that.

Ten weeks later John and Joan were married. Mervyn Whiting, the young man who had brought them together, was the best man.

Following God's Leading

SIX WEEKS AFTER their wedding John was back in India with his bride. He had been asked to take over the management of another plantation some fifty miles west of Dalsingpara. They spent the next year and a half there before being asked to take over the management of the company's largest estate in the same area.

Almost every weekend they would visit the Hares at Raymond Memorial School, at Falakata. Also they became acquainted with the Allan Maberly family, Australians who were at Kalimpong, some eighty miles away. The three families became very good friends.

Sometimes the Maberlys and the Hares would visit John and Joan on their estate. Whenever they were offered tea, they refused it. This would bother John, but he would dismiss the matter from his mind.

One weekend when John and Joan were at Raymond Memorial School, someone preached the Sabbath sermon on the subject of the rich young ruler. The sermon disturbed John. Somehow he

Joan and plantation employees ride an elephant.

felt like that ruler. Certainly his salary was considerably higher than anyone else's in that school building, and he did "rule" over almost three thousand workers. Am I like the rich young ruler, holding on to tea and money rather than Jesus? Is Christ asking me to give up my tea-estate job? And am I turning away from Him? he wondered.

As Joan and he drove back to their estate they discussed the matter, as they did many times afterward. The discussion would always end by John's saying, "I don't know."

The months went by. John was no longer happy. He began to realize that his love for Christ was growing cold because of the business he was in, yet he did not know what he should do.

One day after lunch in early September, 1956, a bearer brought the personal mail to the bungalow. John sat at the table and looked it over. Joan had gone into the living room.

One of the pieces of mail was the mimeographed union paper from union headquarters at Karmatar in the State of Bihar. As he looked through the paper he noticed that the main article was on temperance, by William J. Storz, the union president.

The article dealt with a number of aspects of temperance. Then it began to discuss the subject of tea forthrightly.

Immediately John felt himself resisting the article, but he decided to read it all. Most of it was made up of quotations from the Spirit of Prophecy.

One statement was from *Counsels on Diet and Foods*, page 425: "Tea and coffee drinking is a sin."

John read the statement over again, and yet again. He was stunned.

He got up and went into the living room. Joan was standing near the fireplace.

"Joan, listen to this. Here's an article by Pastor Storz about tea. He's quoted from the Spirit of Prophecy."

He read the statement to her.

"I didn't know that Sister White spoke against tea like that!" Joan exclaimed. "What do we do?"

As they discussed the matter they decided that the

whole matter revolved around the question of whether Ellen White was a true prophet of God or a charlatan, since she claimed to have had visions from God, or whether she had been deluded. If she was truly a servant of God, they would have to accept her word concerning tea and everything else as authoritative.

"If we decide that she is a false prophet, it will not be long before we leave the Adventist Church. If we accept it as a fact that she was God's servant, then this is God's message for us. We will have to give up tea," John observed.

Together they knelt and asked God to guide them and give them courage to face the unknown future, for they knew they would have to leave the tea business.

As they continued to ponder their immediate future they decided they should remain with the plantation for the eighteen months remaining of John's contract, but to notify the company that they would be resigning at the end of the period. They quit drinking tea, and shortly afterward became vegetarians.

In the early spring of 1958 the contract ended, and John and Joan decided to return to England. Elder Rawson suggested that John try colporteur work. The idea interested him, but he also wanted to continue his education, which had been halted by the war.

They were visiting at Joan's parents' home when one day a young man called and asked for John. He introduced himself as Alec Freeman, the assistant publishing secretary for the South England Conference.

As a result of their conversation, John made up his mind to go into the literature evangelistic work.

After attending a beginners' training institute he was assigned the city of Luton as his territory. He chose to sell the set of books, *Footprints of Jesus,* by W. L. Emmerson, editor at the Stanborough Press.

John spent much time in prayer, and God blessed his work. In a short time he was doing well, averaging thirty-five pounds a week in sales, which in 1959 was quite good for a beginner. Soon he was topping the list of bookmen in the union in sales.

In the spring of 1959 he began working in the villages of Bedfordshire, which is John Bunyan country. He found the people very responsive when he suggested prayer in the homes.

In the village of Offley he had called at one home several times, but there was never anyone there. Finally he found the woman at home and was invited in. He was in the middle of his canvass when she interrupted him.

"Mr. Curnow, you will pray in my home too, won't you?"

John's surprise evidently showed on his face, for she said, "You are the man who has been praying in the homes of our village, aren't you?"

"Yes."

"I thought you were. You will pray in my home, won't you?"

"I will be very happy to."

After John had prayed she told him that since he had been visiting the homes in the village the Methodist church had held its first prayer meeting in more than thirty years.

John also had the privilege of selling a set of books to the people living in the cottage where John Bunyan used to live while preaching in the area.

And so John Curnow found the work God had for him to do. Now he knows why his broken bomber, spinning across the runway at Elsham Wolds, loaded with eight thousand pounds of deadly bombs and drenched with its own fuel even as the engines spat fire, did not explode. Now he understands why when death seemed certain in the fiery Lancaster spiraling earthward through the night he came through alive. Now he knows that while death rode the dark wings of night, the protecting hand of a loving God was beneath him.

Epilogue

At the beginning of 1961 John was invited to become the associate publishing secretary of the South England Conference. Eighteen months later he became the secretary, a position he held for two years.

In 1964 he received an invitation from the Southern Asia Division to become publishing department secretary of the South India Union. So once more Joan and he sailed for India, this time to live in the city of Bangalore.

After serving as leader of the publishing work in South India for three years he was asked to become the principal and business manager of Lowry Memorial School, near Bangalore. He was ordained in 1967. In 1969 he became the publishing department secretary of the Southern Asia Division, the headquarters of which is in Poona.

The Curnows have four children in their home. The oldest is demure self-possessed Sally. Then come three lively sons, Adrian, David, and Perryn.

Today John Curnow is happy at his work of leading the literature evangelists of the countries that make up the Southern Asia Division in selling literature that will tell men and women about Jesus Christ.

And he is, understandably, a faithful promoter of the Voice of Prophecy program. On returning from one of his trips in the field he brought back 122 requests for Voice of Prophecy correspondence courses. He had gotten them from men and women to whom he had intro-

John and Joan Curnow with (L-R) Sally, Perryn, David, and Adrian.

duced the course on buses, trains, and planes while he traveled. For he is eager that others who dwell in darkness similar to that in which he lived be led to the dawn of a new day in Christ Jesus.